SOUTHERN STAR FINDER

G000078059

PHILIP'S

SOUTHERN STAR FINDER

A MONTH-BY-MONTH GUIDE TO THE NIGHT SKY

JOHN WOODRUFF AND WIL TIRION

The author would like to thank Neil Bone for his invaluable help in preparing the text.

Text John Woodruff
Star charts Wil Tirion
Editorial consultant Neil Bone
Moon photographs (pp24–25) © UCO/Lick Observatory

First published in Great Britain in 2002 by Philip's, a division of Octopus Publishing Group Limited, 2–4 Heron Quays, London E14 4JP

© 2002 Philip's
Reprinted 2002, 2004 and 2007 (with revisions)

ISBN-10 0 540 08093 4
ISBN-13 978 0 540 08093 9

A CIP catalogue record for this book is available from the British Library.

All rights reserved. Apart from any fair dealing for the purpose of private study, research, criticism or review, as permitted under the Copyright, Designs and Patents Act, 1988, no part of this publication may be reproduced, stored in a retrieval system, or transmitted in any form or by any means, electronic, electrical, chemical, mechanical, optical, photocopying, recording, or otherwise, without prior written permission. All enquiries should be addressed to the Publishers.

Printed in Hong Kong

Details of other Philip's titles and services can be found on our website at: **www.philips-maps.co.uk**

Contents

The Night Sky

Nature has few sights more spectacular than the night sky. On a clear moonless night, even from an urban location, hundreds of stars may be visible. Away from towns and sources of artificial light the spectacle is awesome. The number swells to thousands: seemingly countless stars sparkling against the jet-black depths of space, like brilliant jewels on a velvet backcloth. At first glance the distribution of stars seems random. Look a little longer, and some order emerges - here and there some of the brighter stars form themselves into distinctive patterns. (Some of these patterns can be easier to pick out when fewer stars are visible.) From ancient times, watchers of the sky have sought such patterns among all the stars they could see. These patterns, modified and augmented in more recent times, form the system of *constellations* in use today as a convenient way of locating positions in the night sky.

This book provides the first-time stargazer with a clear and straightforward guide to viewing the stars and constellations on show over the course of the year. The only requirements are reasonable eyesight and a clear sky. The best way to become familiar with the stars is to use what astronomers call the naked eye. Binoculars or a telescope will reveal some spectacular sights. But the best way to get to know the night sky is with your eyes alone.

Stars in Motion

One of the first things that is noticeable about the night sky is that the stars do not move relative to one another. The patterns visible on one night will still be there a week or a year later. (A star-like point that is moving will be an artificial satellite. One that shifts position over the course of weeks or months will be a planet – see page 22.) But, as will become clear after half an hour or so, the whole panoply of stars itself appears to rotate about a fixed point, as if they were on the inside of a giant umbrella, and you were slowly turning the shaft.

Just as the Sun appears to move across the daytime sky, this apparent motion of the stars is a result of the Earth rotating on its axis. The point about which the stars appear to rotate is called the *south celestial pole*. Unfortunately, there is no bright star to mark the position of the south celestial pole; the closest is a dim star called Sigma Octantis. The south celestial pole can be found using the long arm of the Southern Cross (see page 13). Facing the pole you are facing south. All the stars appear to be moving on circular paths around the pole. The farther they are from the pole, the larger the circles they trace out. A long-exposure photograph made by pointing a camera at the south celestial pole for several hours shows the 'trails' of stars as a series of concentric arcs (not full circles, for there are not 24 hours of darkness).

The angle the pole makes with the horizon (called its *altitude*) is the same as your latitude. If you are observing from Sydney (latitude 34°S), the altitude of the pole is 34° – just over one-third of the way from the horizon to the point overhead, called the *zenith*. From any location on Earth between the equator and the poles, the circular paths of the stars are inclined to the horizon – as if the point of the imaginary umbrella were aimed diagonally upwards. Over the course of a night, stars rise at the eastern horizon (just as the Sun does), climb the sky towards the north, then descend to the western horizon, where they set. Which stars are on view thus depends on the time of night.

From any given latitude, some stars

are visible throughout the night. If a star's angular distance* from the south celestial pole is less than the altitude of the pole, it can never set. Such stars are called *circumpolar* (see page 13). From latitudes of just over 40°, for example, the familiar grouping known as the Crux or the Southern Cross is circumpolar. Similarly, there will always be stars permanently out of view. For southern-hemisphere observers, any star whose angular distance from the north celestial pole is less than their latitude can never rise.

Seasonal Changes

So, some stars never set while others never rise. For the rest, it is not only the time of night that determines whether they will be on view, but also the time of year. For example, the constellations that mark the winter sky are not seen in the summer months. To understand why this should be, it is necessary to look at the Earth's rotation on its axis and its orbit around the Sun. The Earth spins on its axis in about 23 hours and 56 minutes. This, the time it takes to return to the same position relative to the stars, is four minutes shorter than the solar day of 24 hours used for timekeeping. The solar day is the time it takes the Earth to return to the same position relative to the Sun. After one complete rotation, it has to turn a little farther on its axis to do this, because of the distance it has travelled in its orbit. This difference means that, in terms of our 24-hour clock, any one star will rise four minutes earlier than on the previous night, or two hours earlier each month. After 12 months, the Earth has completed one orbit of the Sun, the two clocks are back in step, and the stars are back to their same times of rising.

This combined effect of the daily and annual changes in the night sky is reflected in the monthly charts on pages 26–49. The January chart, for example, shows the stars visible on 5 January at 11 p.m. or 20 January at 10 p.m., but also on 20 December at midnight, 6 December at 1 a.m., 5 February at 9 p.m., 20 February at 8 p.m., and for correspondingly later times at earlier dates, and earlier times at later dates (for times which are hours of darkness). When daylight saving time is in operation, subtract an hour from the times given. The striking summer constellation Orion illustrates the seasonal variations in the sky. The January chart shows how it dominates the northern summer sky. By 10–11 p.m. in March Orion is about to set, and does not reappear on the charts until October, when it is rising in the east at around this time.

Constellations

The 88 modern constellations (see page 19) between them cover the whole of the sky. Just over half of them are of ancient origin, and bear the names of people, creatures and objects, mostly from ancient legends. The rest were added from the 16th to the 18th century, to fill the newly charted southern skies and the gaps between the northern constellations occupied by faint stars. Many of the southern constellations named after scientific instruments were introduced by the 18th-century French astronomer Nicolas de Lacaille. The brighter stars also have names. Many of them derive originally from medieval Arab

* It is convenient to measure the separation between two points in the sky as an angle. So, for example, the distance from the zenith to the horizon is 90°. In the same way the Moon is said to have a diameter of ½°.

astronomy, but some have become so corrupted over time that they no longer mean anything in Arabic.

Constellations vary considerably in size and prominence. A few, such as Orion, are unmistakable. Some may be picked out quite easily, while others, even on a very clear night, are very faint and hard to identify. The minor constellations are omitted from the monthly charts on pages 26–49, but are included on the main charts (pages 13–18).

Some prominent groupings of stars are not constellations in their own right, but form part of a larger one. The brightest of these *asterisms*, including the Sickle (part of Leo, the Lion) and the Square of Pegasus, are labelled on the charts.

The ancient astronomers who framed the constellations did not appreciate that stars which appear to be closely grouped in the sky almost always have no association with one another. What look like distinctive triangles, chains and other configurations are invariably made up from stars which lie at very different distances. Their apparent connection is a result of chance: our lines of sight to these stars happen to lie close together. There are exceptions, though. Many of the stars of Scorpius and Centaurus, for example, are moving through space together. And some stars reside in *clusters* – collections of dozens or even thousands of stars closely packed together. The clusters M6 and M7 (page 54) are close enough for their individual members to be visible.

Star Brightnesses

The stars we see in the night sky differ in brightness for two reasons: they lie at different distances from one another, and some are intrinsically more luminous than others. A star's brightness is reckoned according to a scale of *magnitudes* that originated in ancient times. The brightest stars were said to be of first magnitude, those not quite so bright of second magnitude, and so on down to the faintest stars visible, which were sixth magnitude. (The lower the magnitude value, the brighter the star.)

Nowadays the magnitude scale has been put on a proper mathematical footing, and extended to magnitude zero and to negative values for the brightest objects, and to seventh magnitude and beyond for the myriad fainter objects visible in telescopes. Accurate measurements make it possible to quote values to two decimal places. The brightest star, Sirius, has a quoted magnitude of −1.47. A star of magnitude 1.0 is by definition a hundred times as bright as one of magnitude 6.0. A magnitude difference of exactly one corresponds to a difference in brightness of just over 2½. 'First magnitude' means a star between magnitudes 0.5 and 1.5, 'second magnitude' between 1.5 and 2.5, and so on. The monthly charts (pages 26–49) show all stars down to third magnitude, together with fourth-magnitude stars which help to make up some of the fainter constellation patterns. The main charts show all stars down to approximately magnitude 5.0. Some stars are variable – their brightness fluctuates instead of remaining steady (see page 52). Some important variable stars are shown on the charts as a white ring rather than a solid disk.

Although the stars appear white at first glance, the colours of the brightest ones will soon become apparent. A star's colour is an indication of its surface temperature. The coolest stars shine with a red light ('cool' is relative – red stars have a surface temperature of around 3000°C). Orange, yellow, white and blue represent progressively higher surface temperatures. The brightest stars have their colours shown on the charts. Fainter stars are perceived as white for physiological reasons; their colours become apparent when viewed through binoculars or a telescope.

Visibility

Apart from weather conditions, there are various factors that affect the visibility of stars on a given night. For many people the most significant is *light pollution.* At night, towns and cities abound with sources of artificial illumination: not only streetlights, but filling stations, shopfront illuminations, floodlights and security lights. Much of this light is directed upwards, drowning out starlight so that only the brightest stars remain visible. The urban stargazer must be prepared to search out an observing site as far away as possible from such interference.

A natural constraint on star brightness is atmospheric absorption. The lower the altitude of a star, the greater the amount of the Earth's atmosphere its light has to pass through before reaching the observer. Gas molecules in the atmosphere scatter starlight, deflecting some of it away from the observer, which makes stars closer to the horizon appear dimmer. The best time to view a star is therefore when it is highest in the sky. A further factor is eyesight: under ideal conditions, someone with normal vision can see stars of magnitude 6.0, or a little fainter. Some people with extremely good eyesight have claimed to reach magnitude 7.0, and under exceptional conditions even 7.5.

However good your eyesight is, you need to allow some time under the night sky for your eyes to become adjusted to the low light levels. The human eye has two optical systems: day vision and night vision. When you step out into the dark from a brightly lit room, the night vision system takes time to build up to full strength. This process is called *dark adaptation* and for most people takes about 20 to 30 minutes. Subsequent exposure to artificial lights will put you back to square one. If you need to use a torch, use one that shines with a red light as this will not affect your dark adaptation.

The Milky Way

Anyone fortunate enough not to suffer from much light pollution will see, on a clear moonless night, a faint, hazy band of light arching right across the sky. This is the Milky Way – the concentrated light of the vast number of stars that lie between us and the hub of the Galaxy, the huge star system in which the Sun is located. The Galaxy has the overall form of a disk. From our vantage point within it, we see a greater concentration of stars close to the disk's plane than in other directions.

There is a greater concentration of bright stars in and near the Milky Way, which passes through some of the most prominent constellations: Vela, Carina, Crux, Centaurus, Scorpius and Sagittarius in the southern hemisphere, passing close to Orion on the celestial equator, and Aquila, Cygnus, Cassiopeia and Perseus in the northern hemisphere. The Milky Way is shown on the main charts (pages 13–18), but is omitted from the monthly charts.

Ecliptic and Zodiac

The ecliptic is the name given to the path that the Sun appears to follow over the course of the year. (It gets its name from the fact that the Moon has to be on the ecliptic for there to be an eclipse.) Stars along the ecliptic are of course invisible during the daytime, drowned out by the Sun's intense glare. The constellations containing these stars make up the zodiac.

The ecliptic, which is shown on the main charts, is in reality the projection on to the sky of the plane of the Earth's orbit around the Sun. Since most of the other planets of the Solar System orbit the Sun close to this plane, they appear in the sky close to the ecliptic. A bright 'star' near the ecliptic which is not on the charts is most likely a planet (see page 22).

Mapping the Stars

For the purposes of mapping, the most convenient way to conceive of the night sky is as a vast hollow sphere with the Earth at its centre. From wherever we stand on the surface of the Earth, one half of this sphere is visible at any one time, while the other half is invisible. This imaginary sphere is known as the *celestial sphere*. All the stars, though they are at different distances from the Earth, may then be depicted as if they occupied fixed positions on this sphere. (We imagine that the celestial sphere, with the stars fixed upon it, rotates once a day around the Earth, though we know that this isn't so.) Celestial cartographers are then faced with the same problem that confronts terrestrial map-makers: how to represent the curved surface of a sphere on a flat chart. The only essential difference is that terrestrial maps are drawn as if viewed from the outside, whereas celestial charts such as the ones in this book are prepared from an interior vantage point, looking out. The solution is much the same: find a projection that minimizes distortion of constellation shapes. The projections used for the charts in this book are described below.

Coordinates

Like terrestrial maps, celestial charts need to have a reference grid – a system of coordinates – laid upon them so that the positions of objects can be defined unambiguously. On terrestrial maps the coordinates are latitude and longitude. Latitude is measured from 0° to 90° south or north of the equator, while longitude is measured from 0° to 180° east or west of the Greenwich meridian. The celestial equivalents are similar. In place of latitude is *declination*, abbreviated 'dec'. Declination is measured from 0° at the *celestial equator* – the projection on to the celestial sphere of the Earth's equator – up or down to 90° at the celestial poles. A declination value preceded by a minus sign indicates a position in the southern hemisphere: −49°, for example, is above the celestial equator. If there is no sign (or a 'plus' sign) the declination is northerly: 49° (or +49°) is below the celestial equator.

The equivalent of longitude is called *right ascension*, abbreviated 'RA'. Right ascension is traditionally measured not in degrees, but in hours and minutes: from 0 to 24 hours, eastwards around the celestial equator. The starting point, corresponding to an RA of 0 hours – the celestial counterpart of the Greenwich meridian – is chosen to coincide with what is called the vernal equinox. This is the position on the celestial sphere where the Sun, in its annual journey along the ecliptic, crosses the celestial equator travelling from south to north. The vernal equinox lies in the constellation Pisces.

The position of a star or of any other celestial object is thus expressed as, for example, 'RA 6h 45m, dec −17°'.

The Main Charts

The six main charts (pages 13–18) cover the whole of the sky, with some overlap between them. Two show the regions round the south and north celestial poles (Charts 1 and 6), and four show a broad strip of the sky either side of the celestial equator (Charts 2 to 5). They fit together rather like the parts of a food can: Charts 1 and 6 are the top and bottom of the can, and Charts 2 to 5 between them form the cylindrical side. From the latitude of Sydney, the stars on Chart 1 are visible throughout the year. But the stars on Charts 2 to 5, closer to the celestial equator, are not.

Sometimes they are in the daytime sky, and on other occasions they may be visible only shortly after sunset or just before dawn. The seasons and dates when the stars on these charts are highest in the sky at 10 p.m. are at the top of each one. These dates tie in with the monthly charts.

Unavoidably, the projections used do introduce some distortion. This is more of a problem with Charts 2 to 5, which show stars to declinations of 60° south and north of the celestial equator. To depict the constellations in their correct shapes, the declination scale has been stretched at the top and bottom. This has the effect of making constellations on those parts of the charts look rather larger in relation to constellations near the celestial equator, compared with how they appear in the sky.

All 88 constellations are shown on these charts. The constellation names are all in capital letters, while star names are lower case with an initial capital. A few other features, for example prominent asterisms such as the Square of Pegasus, are in italic. The Milky Way is shown in a lighter blue than the main background. The ecliptic (the Sun's path against the background stars) is shown as a dashed red line. The Moon and the planets will always be found near the ecliptic. Over a thousand stars down to about magnitude 5.0 are shown. Each of the six charts has a magnitude scale. The brightest stars are shown in their true colours.

The Monthly Charts

Each pair of monthly charts between them show the whole of the night sky visible from the latitude of Sydney at particular times and dates. These charts are also usable at latitudes further south or north. The only real difference will be with stars near the horizon, which are, in any case, not easy to observe. The difference between chart and sky will become noticeable once you are 15° further south or north. They will serve their purpose very well for observing between the latitudes of 40°S and 60°S.

The main purpose of these charts is to help identify the constellations on view. Only the brightest stars are shown, roughly 200 on each pair of charts, down to third magnitude, with some fourth-magnitude stars to complete distinctive patterns. There is a little distortion resulting from the projection of the dome of the celestial sphere on to the flat page. This has the effect of making constellations near the horizon appear a little stretched.

First, use the calendar index (page 12) to find which pair of charts you need to use. Then locate the south pole as shown on Chart 1 (page 13). When you are facing due south, due west is on your left and east on your right. (West and east are reversed on star charts because they show the view looking up into the sky instead of down towards the ground.) The left-hand chart then shows the view you have to the north. Most of the stars you see will be circumpolar, visible throughout the year.

Now turn and face the opposite direction, north. This is the view that changes most during the course of the year. The Square of Pegasus is a familiar marker in spring skies. Summer is ruled by the bright stars of Orion. Autumn's skies are dominated by Centaurus and Lupus, while winter sees Scorpius at its most prominent, with orange-red Antares and the curl of the Scorpion's 'Sting' riding high.

Calendar Index to the Monthly Charts

To see which pair of monthly charts are appropriate for a particular time and date, find the time at the head of the diagram and follow the vertical column downwards to a point opposite the required date. The diagonal band in which this point lies shows the charts to be consulted. Remember to subtract one hour from your clock time if daylight saving time is in operation.

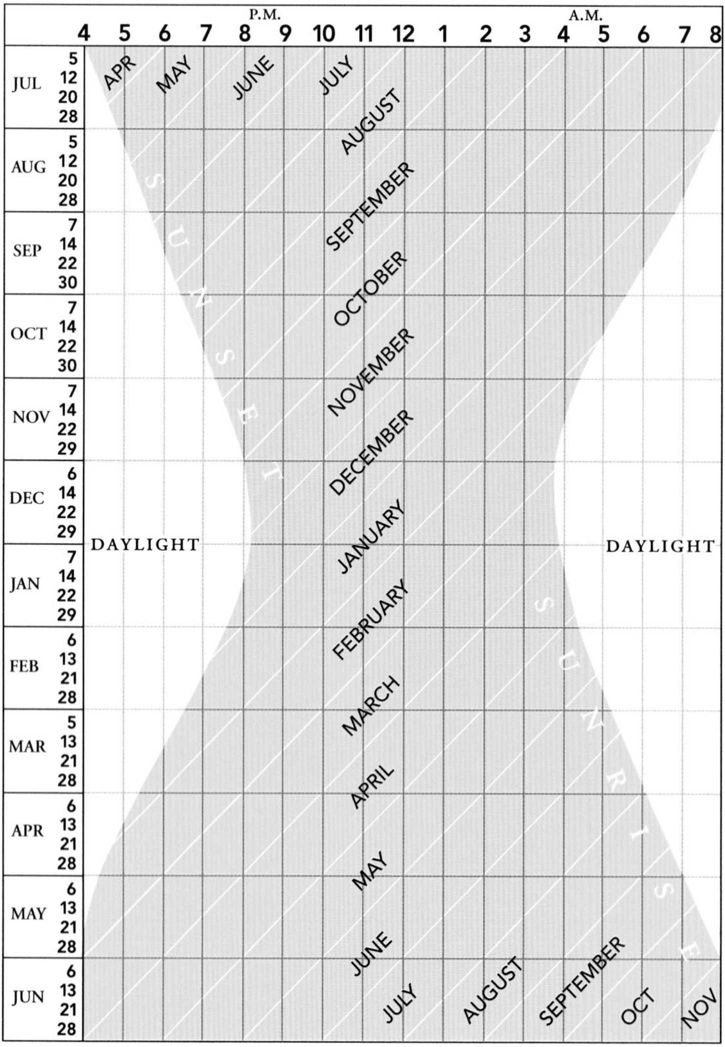

Chart 1: Southern Circumpolar Stars

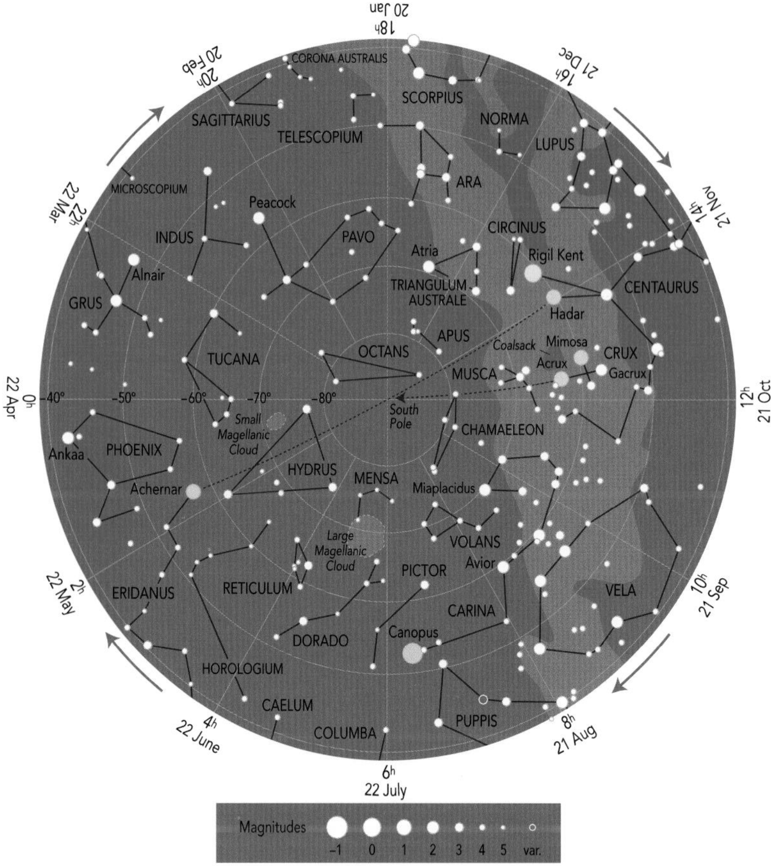

This chart extends to 51½° from the south celestial pole, to a declination of −38½°. Stars out to declination −56° are circumpolar as viewed from the latitude of Sydney (latitude 34°S) – in other words, from this latitude, these stars are above the horizon throughout the year. Unlike its northern equivalent, the south celestial pole is not marked by a prominent star. Shown on the chart are two ways of locating it. The stars of the constellation Crux point towards the pole, which is also almost halfway between the bright stars Achernar, in Eridanus, and Hadar, in Centaurus.

The dates round the outside indicate when the lines of right ascension, making up the radial spokes of the coordinate grid, are aligned with the south point of the horizon at 10 p.m. For instance, on 22 April the 0h line of right ascension is to the north. Phoenix is quite low in the south, while on the opposite side of the pole the stars of Crux are high in the sky. The arrows indicate the apparent motion of the stars. Two hours of right ascension correspond to two hours of time. So, for example, by 12 p.m. on 22 April the sky will have rotated to bring Achernar to just above the south point of the horizon, and the 'bottom' of the chart will now be the point marked 2h/22 May.

Chart 2: Autumn/Winter

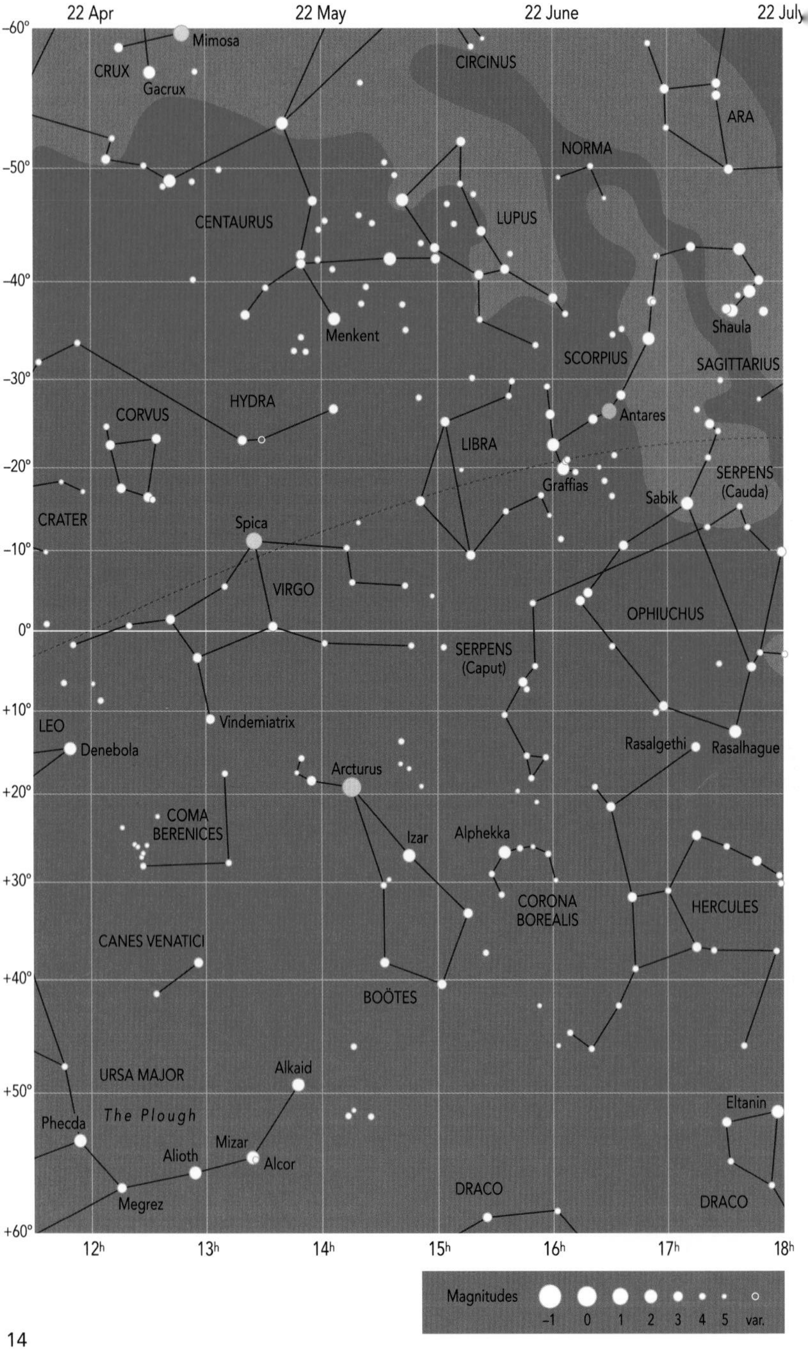

Chart 3: Winter/Spring

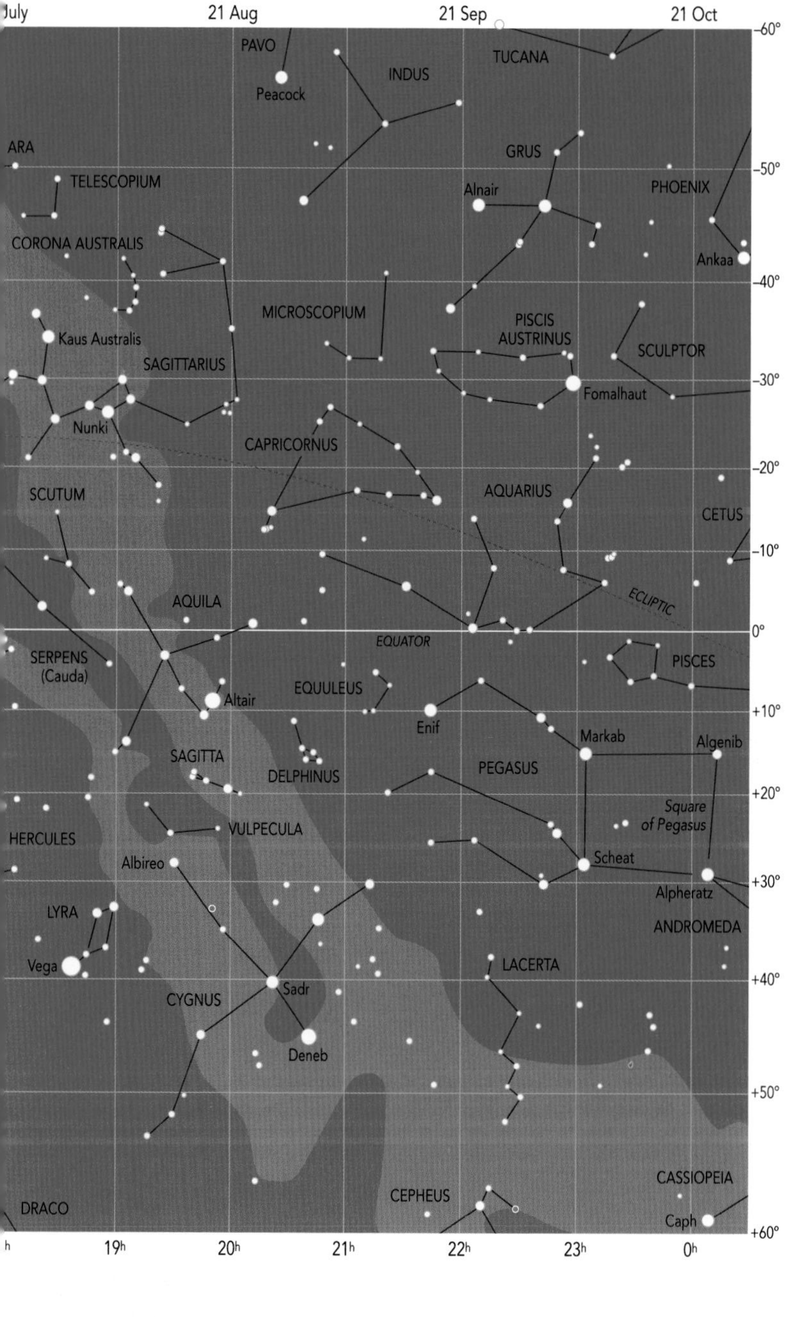

Chart 4: Spring/Summer

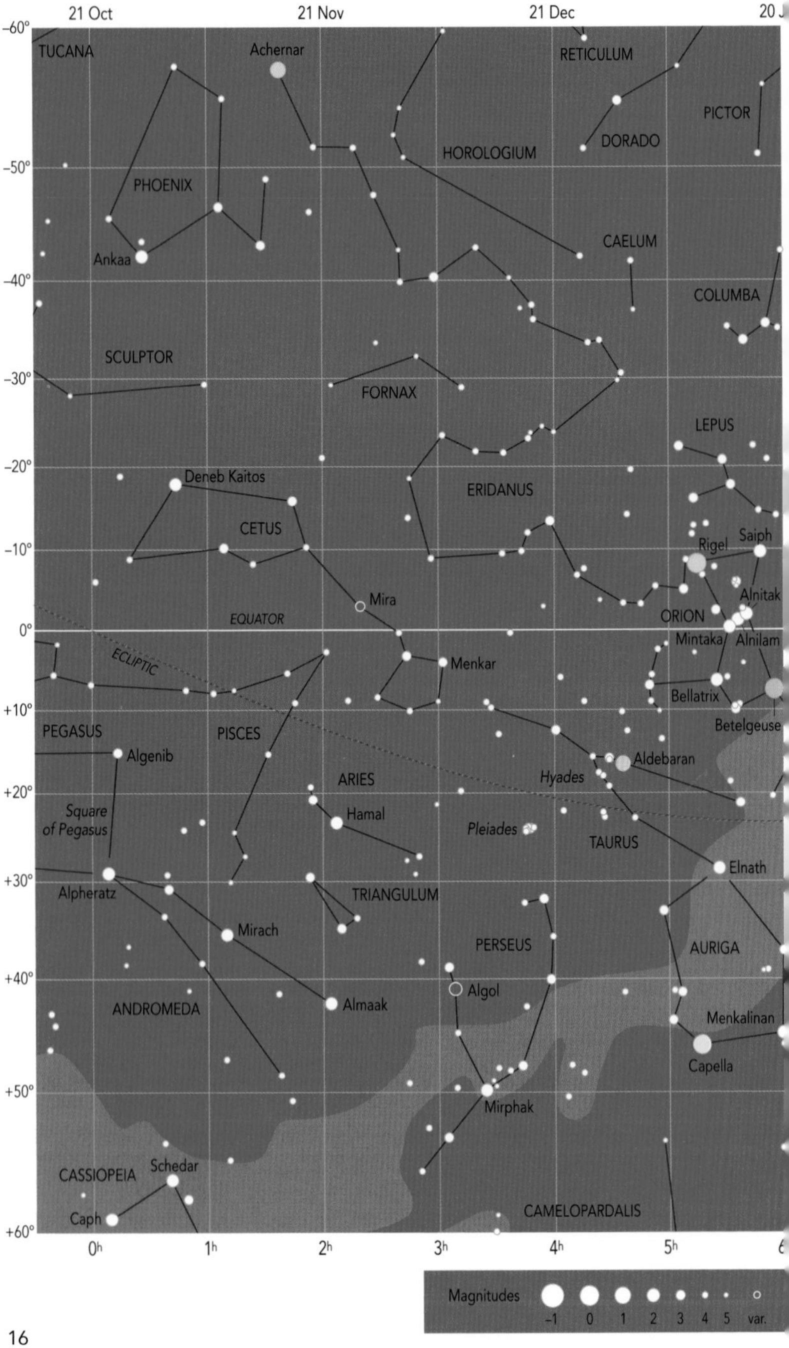

Chart 5: Summer/Autumn

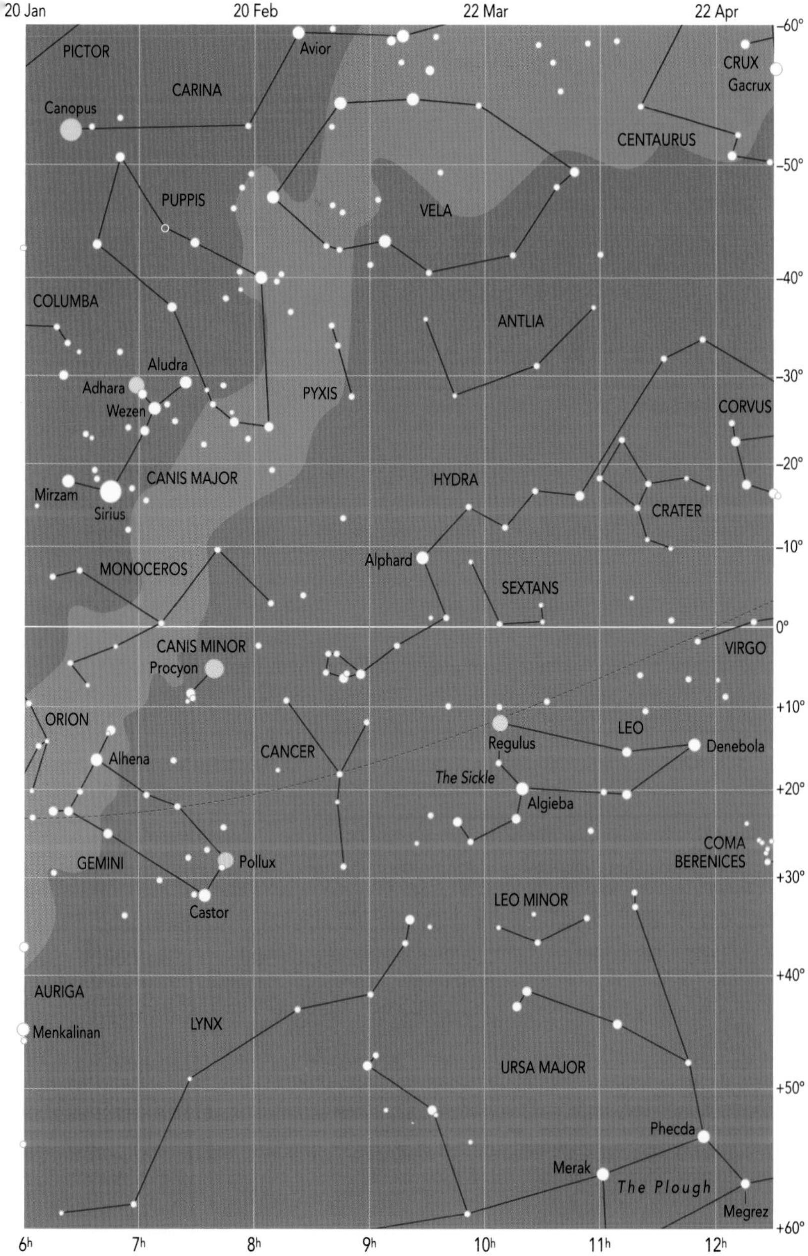

Chart 6: Northern Circumpolar Stars

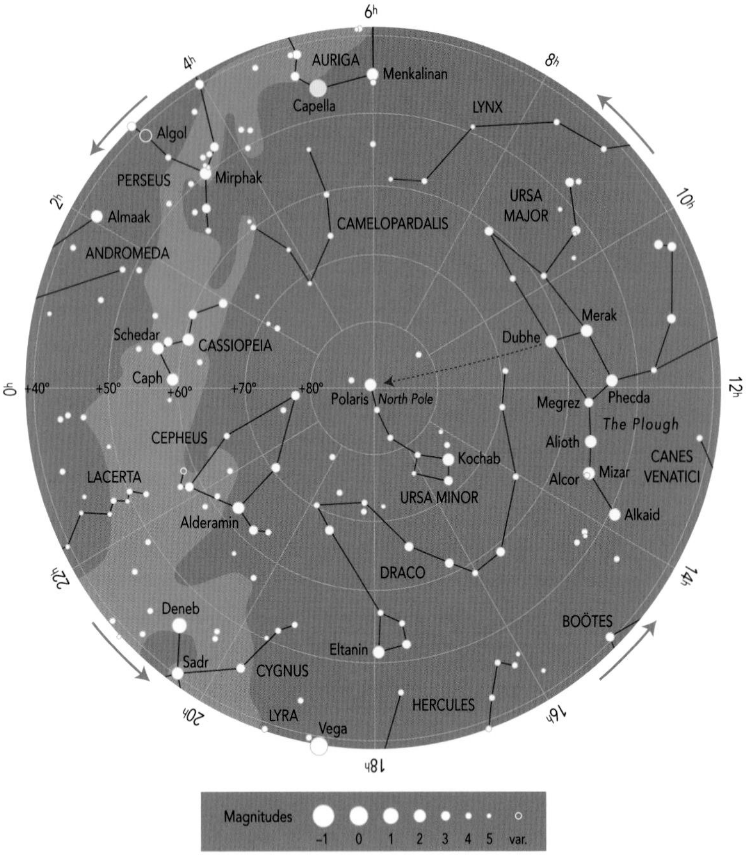

This chart extends out to 51½° from the north celestial pole. It thus shows stars which are circumpolar as viewed from the latitude of London – in other words, from southerly latitudes, these stars are below the horizon throughout the year.

Unlike the situation in the southern hemisphere, the north celestial pole is conveniently marked by a prominent star, appropriately named Polaris. Observers can easily identify Polaris by extending a line from the stars known as the 'Pointers' (Merak and Dubhe) in the Plough.

The Constellations

The constellations and their names are approved by the International Astronomical Union.

Constellation	English name	Chart
Andromeda	Andromeda	3, 4, 6
Antlia	Air Pump	5
Apus	Bird of Paradise	1
Aquarius	Water Carrier	3
Aquila	Eagle	3
Ara	Altar	1, 2, 3
Aries	Ram	4
Auriga	Charioteer	4, 5, 6
Boötes	Herdsman	2, 6
Caelum	Chisel	1, 4
Camelopardalis	Giraffe	4, 6
Cancer	Crab	5
Canes Venatici	Hunting Dogs	2, 6
Canis Major	Great Dog	5
Canis Minor	Little Dog	5
Capricornus	Sea-Goat	3
Carina	Keel	1, 5
Cassiopeia	Cassiopeia	3, 4, 6
Centaurus	Centaur	1, 2, 5
Cepheus	Cepheus	3, 6
Cetus	Whale	3, 4
Chamaeleon	Chameleon	1
Circinus	Compasses	1, 2
Columba	Dove	1, 4, 5
Coma Berenices	Berenice's Hair	2, 5
Corona Australis	Southern Crown	1, 3
Corona Borealis	Northern Crown	2
Corvus	Crow	2, 5
Crater	Cup	2, 5
Crux	Cross	1, 2, 5
Cygnus	Swan	3, 6
Delphinus	Dolphin	3
Dorado	Swordfish	1, 4
Draco	Dragon	2, 3, 6
Equuleus	Foal	3
Eridanus	River Eridanus	1, 4
Fornax	Furnace	4
Gemini	Twins	5
Grus	Crane	1, 3
Hercules	Hercules	2, 3, 6
Horologium	Clock	1, 4
Hydra	Water Snake	2, 5
Hydrus	Little Water Snake	1
Indus	Indian	1, 3

Constellation	English name	Chart
Lacerta	Lizard	6
Leo	Lion	2, 5
Leo Minor	Little Lion	5
Lepus	Hare	4
Libra	Scales	2
Lupus	Wolf	1, 2
Lynx	Lynx	5, 6
Lyra	Lyre	3, 6
Mensa	Table Mountain	1
Microscopium	Microscope	1, 3
Monoceros	Unicorn	5
Musca	Fly	1
Norma	Square	1, 2
Octans	Octant	1
Ophiuchus	Serpent Bearer	2
Orion	Orion	4, 5
Pavo	Peacock	1, 3
Pegasus	Winged Horse	3, 4
Perseus	Perseus	4, 6
Phoenix	Phoenix	1, 3, 4
Pictor	Painter's Easel	1, 4, 5
Pisces	Fishes	3, 4
Piscis Austrinus	Southern Fish	3
Puppis	Poop	1, 5
Pyxis	Ship's Compass	5
Reticulum	Net	1, 4
Sagitta	Arrow	3
Sagittarius	Archer	1, 2, 3
Scorpius	Scorpion	1, 2
Sculptor	Sculptor	3, 4
Scutum	Shield	3
Serpens	Serpent	2, 3
Sextans	Sextant	5
Taurus	Bull	4
Telescopium	Telescope	1, 3
Triangulum	Triangle	4
Triangulum Australe	Southern Triangle	1
Tucana	Toucan	1, 3, 4
Ursa Major	Great Bear	2, 5, 6
Ursa Minor	Little Bear	6
Vela	Sails	1, 5
Virgo	Virgin	2, 5
Volans	Flying Fish	1
Vulpecula	Fox	3

Star Names

Listed here are all the stars named on the charts. They include all the brightest stars. Unlike constellation names, star names have no official status. There are many spelling variants: Almaak, for example, is sometimes spelt Almach or Alamak. Variant names also exist: Hadar, for example, is also known as Agena.

Star	Chart	Position RA	Position dec	Magnitude	Constellation
Achernar	1, 4	1h 38m	−57°	0.5	Eridanus
Acrux	1	12h 27m	−63°	0.8	Crux
Adhara	5	6h 59m	−29°	1.5	Canis Major
Albireo	3	19h 31m	28°	2.9	Cygnus
Alcor	2, 6	13h 25m	55°	4.0	Ursa Major
Aldebaran	4	4h 36m	17°	0.9	Taurus
Alderamin	6	21h 19m	63°	2.4	Cepheus
Algenib	3, 4	0h 13m	15°	2.8	Pegasus
Algieba	5	10h 20m	20°	1.9	Leo
Algol	4, 6	3h 08m	41°	2.1	Perseus
Alhena	5	6h 38m	16°	1.9	Gemini
Alioth	2, 6	12h 54m	56°	1.8	Ursa Major
Alkaid	2, 6	13h 48m	49°	1.9	Ursa Major
Almaak	4, 6	2h 04m	42°	2.3	Andromeda
Alnair	1, 3	22h 08m	−47°	1.7	Grus
Alnilam	4	5h 36m	−1°	1.7	Orion
Alnitak	4	5h 41m	−2°	1.9	Orion
Alphard	5	9h 28m	−9°	2.0	Hydra
Alphekka	2	15h 35m	27°	2.2	Corona Borealis
Alpheratz	3, 4	0h 08m	29°	2.1	Andromeda/Pegasus
Altair	3	19h 51m	9°	0.8	Aquila
Aludra	5	7h 24m	−29°	2.5	Canis Major
Ankaa	1, 3, 4	0h 26m	−42°	2.4	Phoenix
Antares	2	16h 29m	−26°	0.9	Scorpius
Arcturus	2	14h 16m	19°	0.0	Boötes
Atria	1	16h 49m	−69°	1.9	Triangulum Australe
Avior	1, 5	8h 23m	−60°	1.9	Carina
Bellatrix	4	5h 25m	6°	1.6	Orion
Betelgeuse	4	5h 55m	7°	0.5	Orion
Canopus	5	6h 24m	−53°	−0.7	Carina
Capella	4, 6	5h 17m	46°	0.1	Auriga
Caph	3, 4, 6	0h 09m	59°	2.3	Cassiopeia
Castor	5	7h 35m	32°	1.8	Gemini
Deneb Kaitos	4	0h 44m	−18°	2.0	Cetus
Deneb	3, 6	20h 41m	45°	1.3	Cygnus
Denebola	2, 5	11h 49m	15°	2.1	Leo
Dubhe	6	11h 04m	62°	1.8	Ursa Major
Elnath	4	5h 26m	29°	1.7	Taurus
Eltanin	2, 6	17h 57m	51°	2.2	Draco
Enif	6	21h 44m	10°	2.4	Pegasus

Star	Chart	Position		Magnitude	Constellation
		RA	dec		
Fomalhaut	3	22h 58m	−30°	1.2	Piscis Austrinus
Gacrux	1, 2, 5	12h 31m	−57°	1.6	Crux
Graffias	2	16h 05m	−20°	2.6	Scorpius
Hadar	1	14h 04m	−60°	0.6	Centaurus
Hamal	4	2h 07m	23°	2.0	Aries
Izar	2	14h 45m	27°	2.4	Boötes
Kaus Australis	3	18h 24m	−34°	1.9	Sagittarius
Kochab	6	14h 51m	74°	2.1	Ursa Minor
Markab	3	23h 05m	15°	2.5	Pegasus
Megrez	2, 5, 6	12h 15m	57°	3.3	Ursa Major
Menkalinan	4, 5, 6	6h 00m	45°	1.9	Auriga
Menkar	4	3h 02m	4°	2.5	Cetus
Menkent	2	14h 07m	−36°	2.1	Centaurus
Merak	5, 6	11h 02m	56°	2.4	Ursa Major
Miaplacidus	1	9h 13m	−70°	1.7	Carina
Mimosa	1, 2	12h 48m	−60°	1.2	Crux
Mintaka	4	5h 32m	0°	2.2	Orion
Mira	4	2h 19m	−3°	2.0	Cetus
Mirach	4	1h 10m	36°	2.1	Andromeda
Mirphak	4, 6	3h 24m	50°	1.8	Perseus
Mirzam	5	6h 23m	−18°	2.0	Canis Major
Mizar	2, 6	13h 24m	55°	2.3	Ursa Major
Nunki	3	18h 55m	−26°	2.0	Sagittarius
Peacock	1, 3	20h 26m	−57°	1.9	Pavo
Phecda	2, 5, 6	11h 54m	54°	2.4	Ursa Major
Polaris	6	2h 31m	89°	2.0	Ursa Minor
Pollux	5	7h 45m	28°	1.1	Gemini
Procyon	5	7h 39m	5°	0.4	Canis Minor
Rasalgethi	2	17h 15m	14°	3.1	Hercules
Rasalhague	2	17h 35m	13°	2.1	Ophiuchus
Regulus	5	10h 08m	12°	1.4	Leo
Rigel	4	5h 15m	−8°	0.1	Orion
Rigil Kent	1	14h 40m	−61°	−0.3	Centaurus
Sabik	2	17h 10m	−16°	2.4	Ophiuchus
Sadr	3, 6	20h 22m	40°	2.2	Cygnus
Saiph	4	5h 48m	−10°	2.1	Orion
Scheat	3	23h 04m	28°	2.4	Pegasus
Schedar	4, 6	0h 41m	57°	2.2	Cassiopeia
Shaula	2	17h 34m	−37°	1.6	Scorpius
Sirius	5	6h 45m	−17°	−1.5	Canis Major
Spica	2	13h 25m	−11°	1.0	Virgo
Vega	3, 6	18h 37m	39°	0.0	Lyra
Vindemiatrix	2	13h 02m	11°	2.8	Virgo
Wezen	5	7h 08m	−26°	1.8	Canis Major

Positions are to the nearest minute of RA and degree of declination. Magnitudes are correct to one decimal place. The magnitudes of double stars are combined, and those of variable stars are for maximum brightness.

The Planets

Any bright 'star' which you see near the ecliptic but is not on the star charts is almost certainly a planet. The planets cannot be plotted on star charts because they are continually changing their positions in the sky as they move in their orbits around the Sun. Six of the planets are bright enough to be seen from the Earth with the naked eye. They are, in order of their orbits around the Sun, Mercury, Venus, Mars, Jupiter, Saturn and Uranus. Uranus is very faint, but the other five rival and sometimes even outshine the brightest stars – Venus can actually be seen in the daytime, if you know exactly where to look.*

Mercury and Venus orbit closer to the Sun than the Earth does, and so are never far from the Sun in the sky. Mercury, the innermost planet, is so close to the Sun that it is glimpsed only occasionally in the twilight shortly after sunset or shortly before sunrise. Venus, though, may be visible as a brilliant beacon for over two hours after the Sun sets, when it is known as the evening star, or before the Sun rises, when it is called the morning star. Venus at its brightest has a magnitude of −4.7, 20 times as bright as Sirius, the brightest star. Mercury can reach magnitude −1.7, but never seems particularly bright as it is always viewed near the horizon in a twilit sky.

Both these planets orbit the Sun quite quickly, and their positions in the sky are seen to change over the course of a few nights. But Mars, Jupiter and Saturn have orbits outside the Earth's and consequently move more slowly. They take, respectively, nearly two years, nearly 12 years, and 29½ years to orbit the Sun. Although the change in position of Mars soon becomes noticeable, Jupiter and, in particular, Saturn will need to be observed for several weeks before their motion against the stars of the zodiacal constellations is apparent.

After Venus, Jupiter is the brightest of the planets, reaching magnitude −2.9 when its orbit brings it nearest the Earth. Saturn at its brightest is magnitude −0.8. These two are giant planets, around ten times the Earth's diameter. But Mars is small – half the size of the Earth – and its distance from the Earth varies widely over the course of its orbit. Its brightness therefore also varies widely, but at maximum it rivals Jupiter, at magnitude −2.8.

The tables on the opposite page show where to locate Venus, Mars, Jupiter and Saturn on the main charts for each month of the year up to December 2011. (As Mercury orbits the Sun in only 88 days, its positions cannot be plotted at monthly intervals.) The tables give the planet's right ascension (RA), in hours and minutes, for the first day of each month. Look up the RA for the date nearest the one you require, and find this RA value along the bottom edge of Charts 2 to 5. (For the faster-moving Venus and Mars, it may help to estimate an intermediate RA for a position near the middle of a month.) The RA values are correct to the nearest 4 minutes. On the scale of Charts 2 to 5, this corresponds very nearly to 1 mm. Now imagine a line drawn vertically up the chart from the point you have located. The planet will be found close to the position where this line crosses the ecliptic. The tables can also be used in reverse, to identify a planet. Estimate its RA by locating nearby stars on the charts, then consult the tables to see which planet should be near that position.

* Don't look for Venus when it is near the Sun: you will risk permanent damage to your eyesight, and in any case the planet will be invisible in the Sun's glare. And *never* look at the Sun through binoculars or a telescope.

VENUS

Year	Jan	Feb	Mar	Apr	May	Jun	Jul	Aug	Sep	Oct	Nov	Dec
2007	19 52	22 28	00 36	02 56	05 24	07 52	09 40	10 12	09 12	09 44	11 32	13 36
2008	16 00	18 40	21 12	23 40	01 56	04 28	07 08	09 44	12 08	14 24	17 00	19 36
2009	22 00	23 52	00 44	00 04	00 08	01 36	03 36	06 00	08 36	11 00	13 20	15 48
2010	18 40	21 23	23 37	01 58	04 25	07 08	09 33	11 40	13 26	14 31	13 56	13 57
2011	15 32	17 49	20 07	22 35	00 51	03 14	05 48	08 31	11 02	13 19	15 49	18 30
2012	21 07	23 29	01 31	03 37	05 15	05 10	04 26	05 35	07 41	09 58	12 17	14 36
2013	17 15	20 03	22 23	00 46	03 07	05 48	08 26	10 53	13 06	15 17	17 40	19 34
2014	19 53	18 55	19 48	21 47	23 53	02 07	04 29	07 09	09 47	12 07	14 31	17 06

MARS

Year	Jan	Feb	Mar	Apr	May	Jun	Jul	Aug	Sep	Oct	Nov	Dec
2007	17 08	18 48	20 20	21 56	23 40	00 48	02 12	03 36	04 56	06 04	06 48	06 48
2008	06 00	05 32	05 56	06 48	07 52	09 00	10 08	11 20	12 32	13 36	15 08	16 36
2009	18 16	19 56	21 28	23 00	00 24	01 52	03 20	04 48	06 16	07 36	08 40	09 24
2010	09 29	08 49	08 16	08 24	09 04	10 00	11 00	12 07	13 19	14 36	16 05	17 40
2011	19 23	21 04	22 31	00 01	01 26	02 55	04 24	05 56	07 24	08 42	09 52	10 48
2012	11 28	11 39	11 10	10 31	10 31	11 05	11 55	12 58	14 11	15 32	17 07	18 46
2013	20 29	22 06	23 28	00 56	02 22	03 52	05 22	06 53	08 19	09 35	10 47	11 49
2014	12 45	13 29	13 46	13 24	12 44	12 36	13 06	14 01	15 14	16 39	18 17	19 56

JUPITER

Year	Jan	Feb	Mar	Apr	May	Jun	Jul	Aug	Sep	Oct	Nov	Dec
2007	16 28	16 52	17 08	17 16	17 12	16 56	16 44	16 32	16 36	16 52	17 16	17 44
2008	18 12	18 44	19 08	19 28	19 36	19 32	19 20	19 04	18 56	19 00	19 12	19 36
2009	20 04	20 36	21 00	21 28	21 44	21 56	21 56	21 48	21 32	21 20	21 24	21 36
2010	21 56	22 22	22 48	23 15	23 39	00 00	00 12	00 14	00 06	23 51	23 40	23 39
2011	23 50	00 09	00 31	00 58	01 25	01 51	02 12	02 28	02 33	02 27	02 12	01 59
2012	01 54	02 03	02 18	02 44	03 11	03 41	04 09	04 34	04 53	05 00	04 55	04 40
2013	04 24	04 17	04 23	04 41	05 05	05 34	06 04	06 34	07 00	07 19	07 28	07 24
2014	07 09	06 52	06 45	06 49	07 04	07 27	07 54	08 23	08 50	09 13	09 31	09 40

SATURN

Year	Jan	Feb	Mar	Apr	May	Jun	Jul	Aug	Sep	Oct	Nov	Dec
2007	09 48	09 40	09 32	09 24	09 24	09 32	09 40	09 56	10 08	10 24	10 36	10 40
2008	10 44	10 36	10 28	10 20	10 16	10 20	10 28	10 40	10 56	11 08	11 20	11 28
2009	11 32	11 32	11 24	11 16	11 08	11 08	11 12	11 24	11 36	11 52	12 04	12 16
2010	12 20	12 20	12 14	12 06	11 59	11 56	11 59	12 07	12 19	12 32	12 46	12 57
2011	03 05	03 07	03 04	12 56	12 48	12 43	12 43	12 49	13 00	13 12	13 26	13 39
2012	13 48	13 53	13 51	13 45	13 36	13 29	13 27	13 31	13 40	13 52	14 06	14 19
2013	14 31	14 38	14 39	14 34	14 25	14 17	14 13	14 14	14 21	14 32	14 46	15 00
2014	15 13	15 22	15 25	15 23	15 15	15 06	15 00	14 59	15 04	15 14	15 27	15 42

The Moon

When strong moonlight makes it difficult to observe the stars, turn your attention to the Moon itself. Some of its features are marked on this pair of photographs, showing the Moon at last quarter, a week after it is full (right), and at first quarter, a week before it is full (left). The largest of these features are apparent to the naked eye. Binoculars or a small telescope will show many more.

'Mare' means 'sea'. Astronomers once thought that the Moon was Earth-like, but

these dark areas are in fact solidified lava which flooded into giant impact craters formed when the Moon was young. The maria have rather fanciful names: Oceanus Procellarum means 'Ocean of Storms', while Mare Serenitatis is the 'Sea of Serenity'. The craters are named mostly after famous astronomers of the past.

The visibility of lunar features depends on the Moon's phase. At full Moon, for example, the surface appears very bright and some features are hard to see.

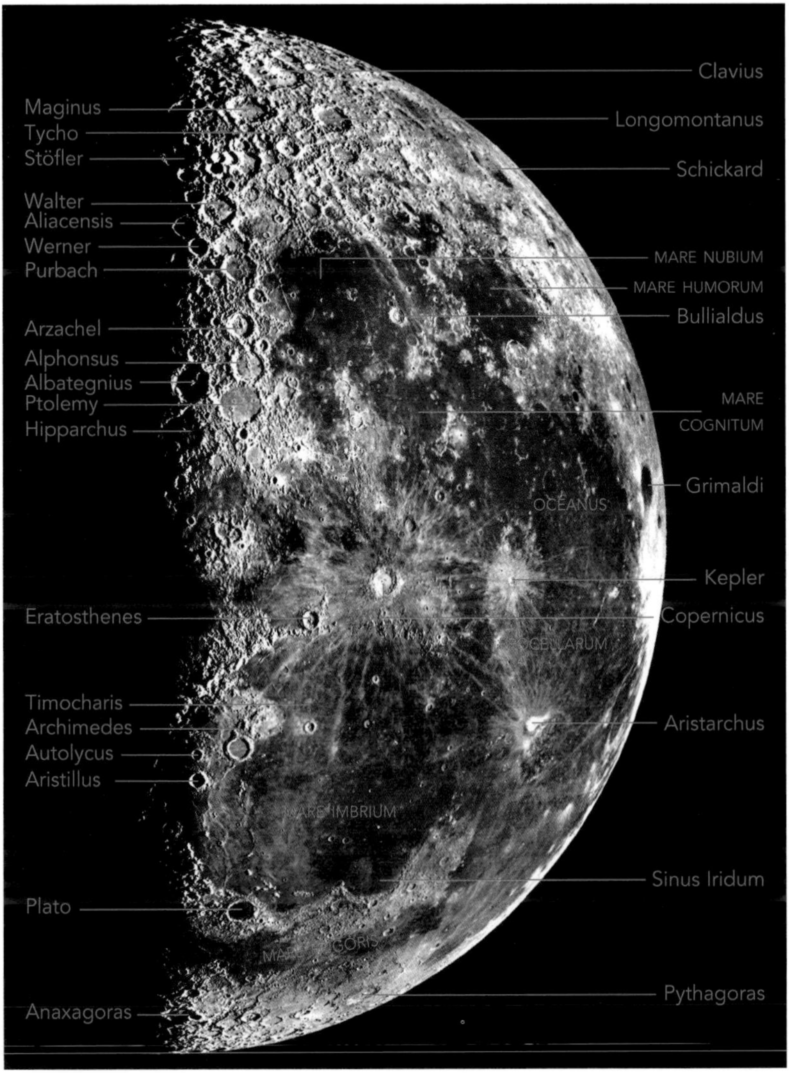

January – Looking North

The main constellations visible on January evenings. The positions are correct for 5 January at 11 p.m. and 20 January at 10 p.m. Use this pair of charts for other dates and times in January, for four minutes later each previous night, or four minutes earlier each following night: for example, 4 January at 11.04 p.m., 6 January at 10.56 p.m. or 10 January at 10.40 p.m.

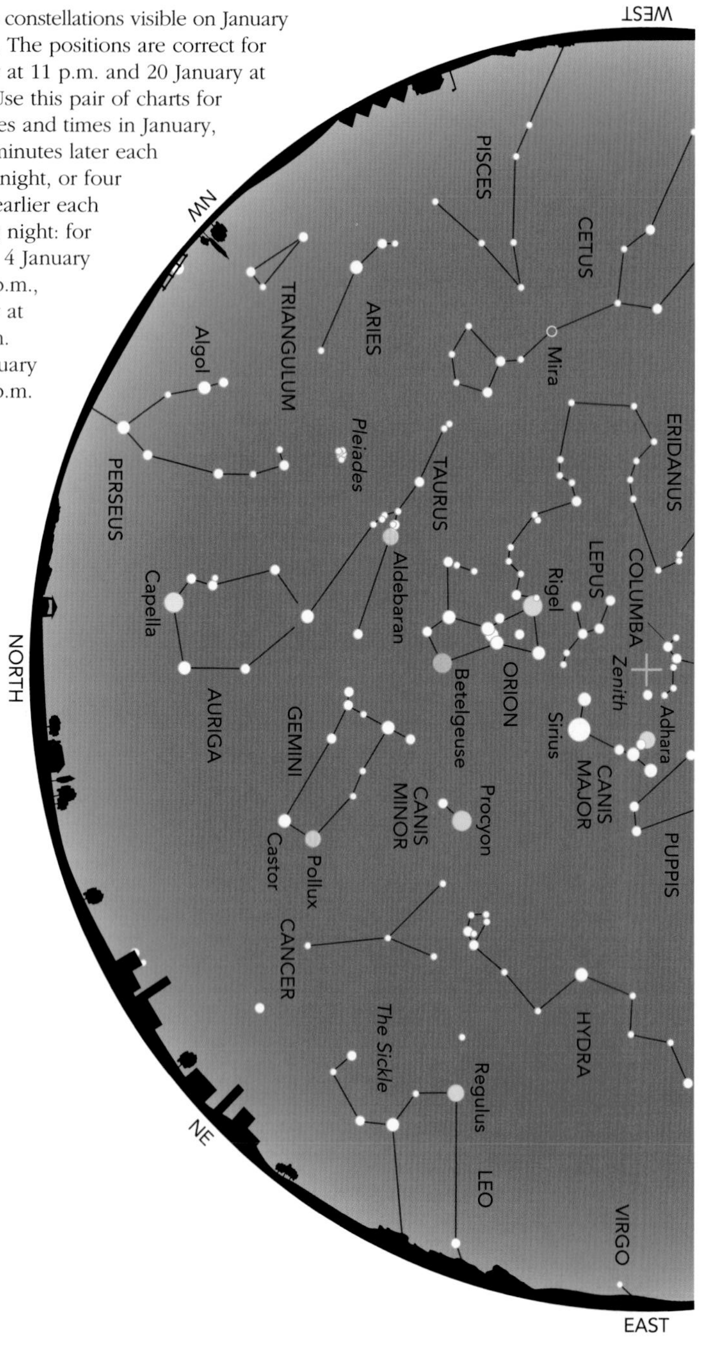

January – Looking South

Times in other months for which the chart may be used are indicated in the calendar index (page 12). In two hours the celestial sphere rotates so that the stars will have moved from the positions shown here to those shown on the February charts.

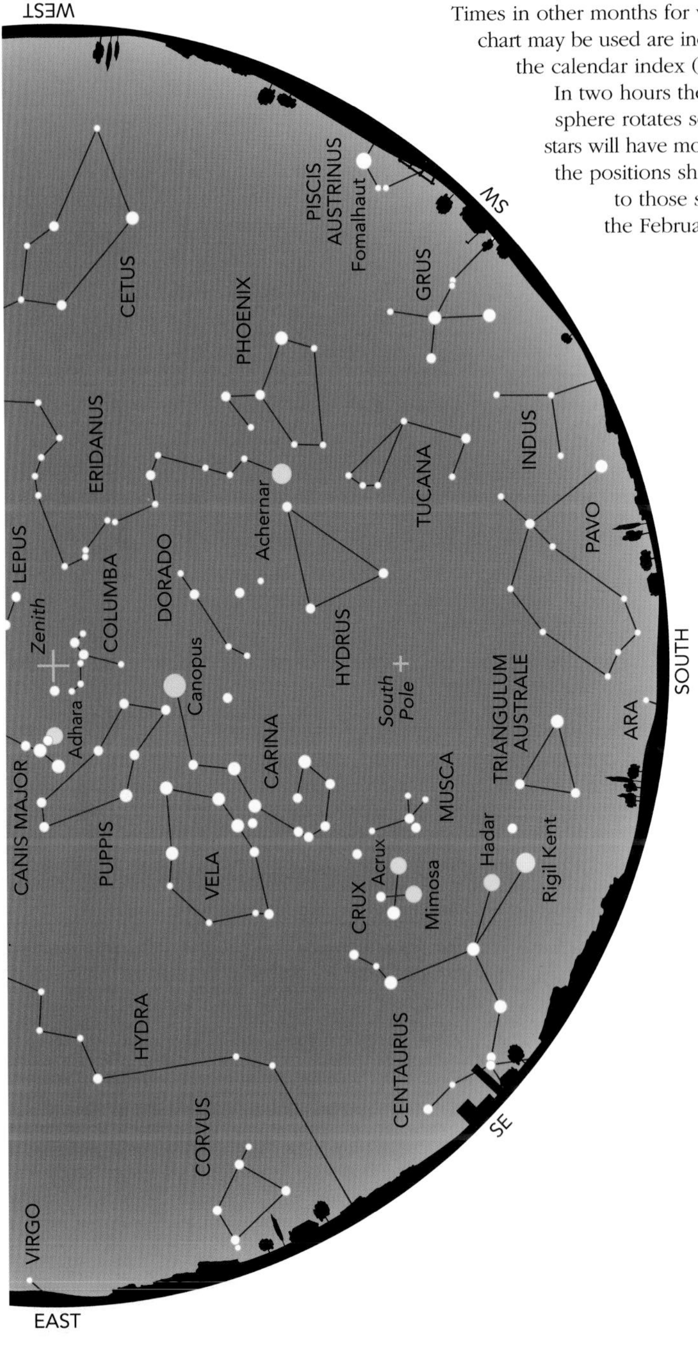

February – Looking North

The main constellations visible on February evenings. The positions are correct for 5 February at 11 p.m. and 20 February at 10 p.m. Use this pair of charts for other dates and times in February, for four minutes later each previous night, or four minutes earlier each following night: for example, 4 February at 11.04 p.m., 6 February at 10.56 p.m. or 10 February at 10.40 p.m.

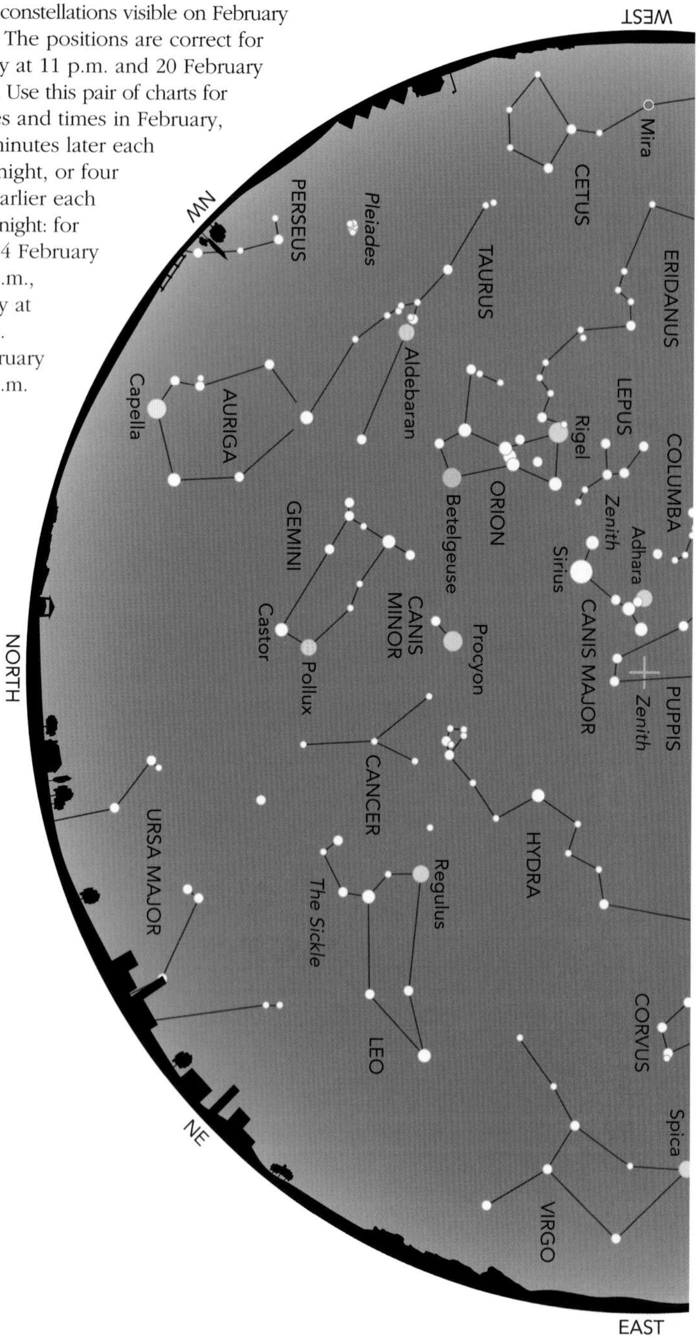

February – Looking South

Times in other months for which the chart may be used are indicated in the calendar index (page 12). In two hours the celestial sphere rotates so that the stars will have moved from the positions shown here to those shown on the March charts.

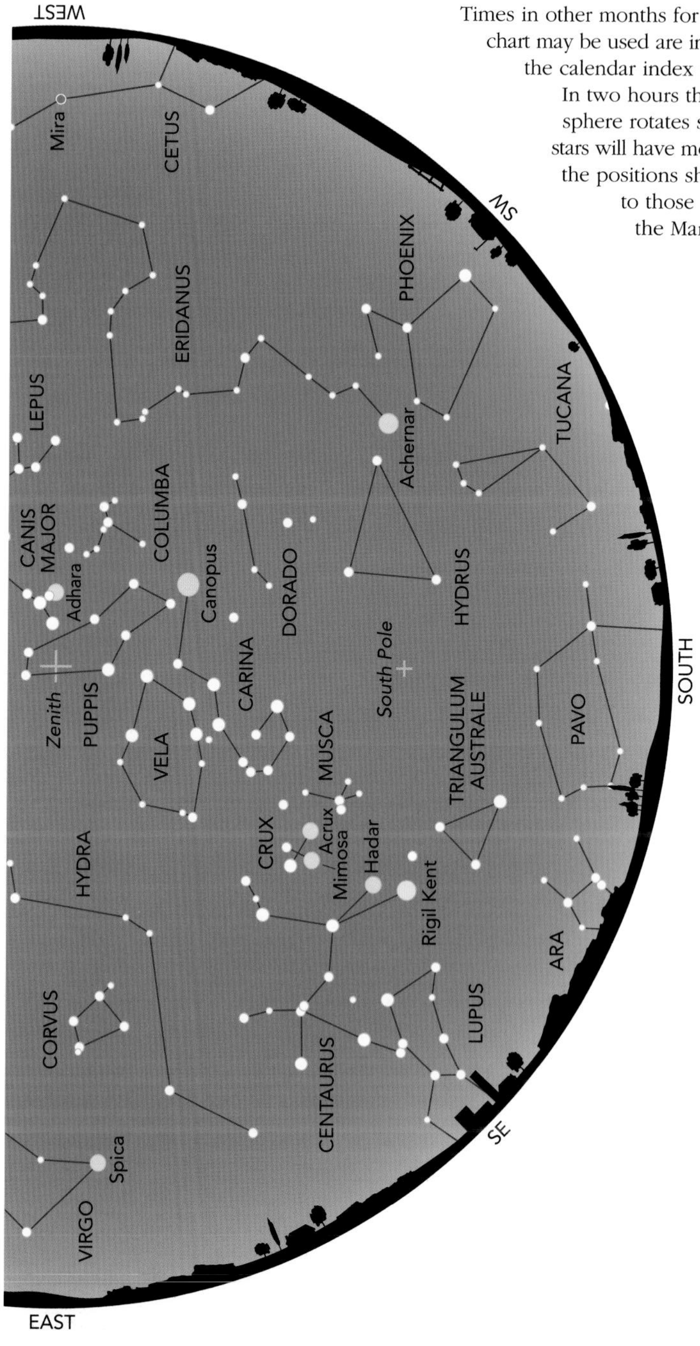

March – Looking North

The main constellations visible on March evenings. The positions are correct for 5 March at 11 p.m. and 20 March at 10 p.m. Use this pair of charts for other dates and times in March, for four minutes later each previous night, or four minutes earlier each following night: for example, 4 March at 11.04 p.m., 6 March at 10.56 p.m. or 10 March at 10.40 p.m.

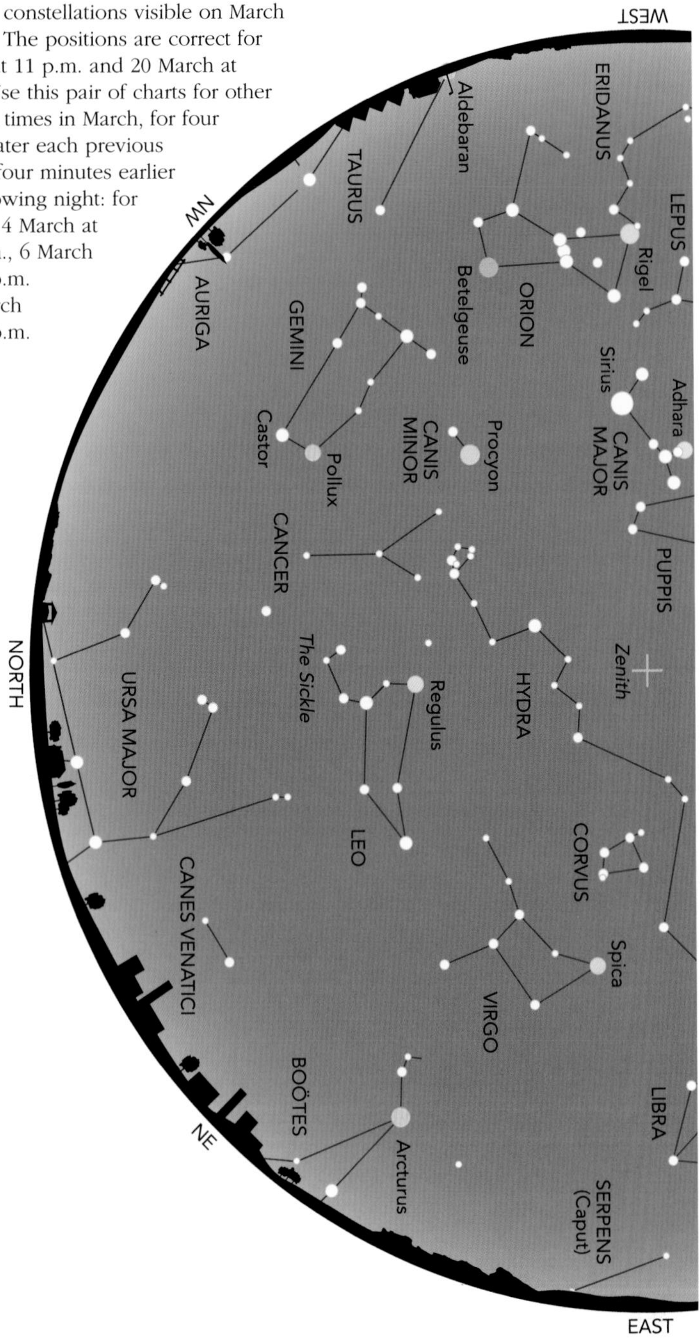

March – Looking South

Times in other months for which the chart may be used are indicated in the calendar index (page 12). In two hours the celestial sphere rotates so that the stars will have moved from the positions shown here to those shown on the April charts.

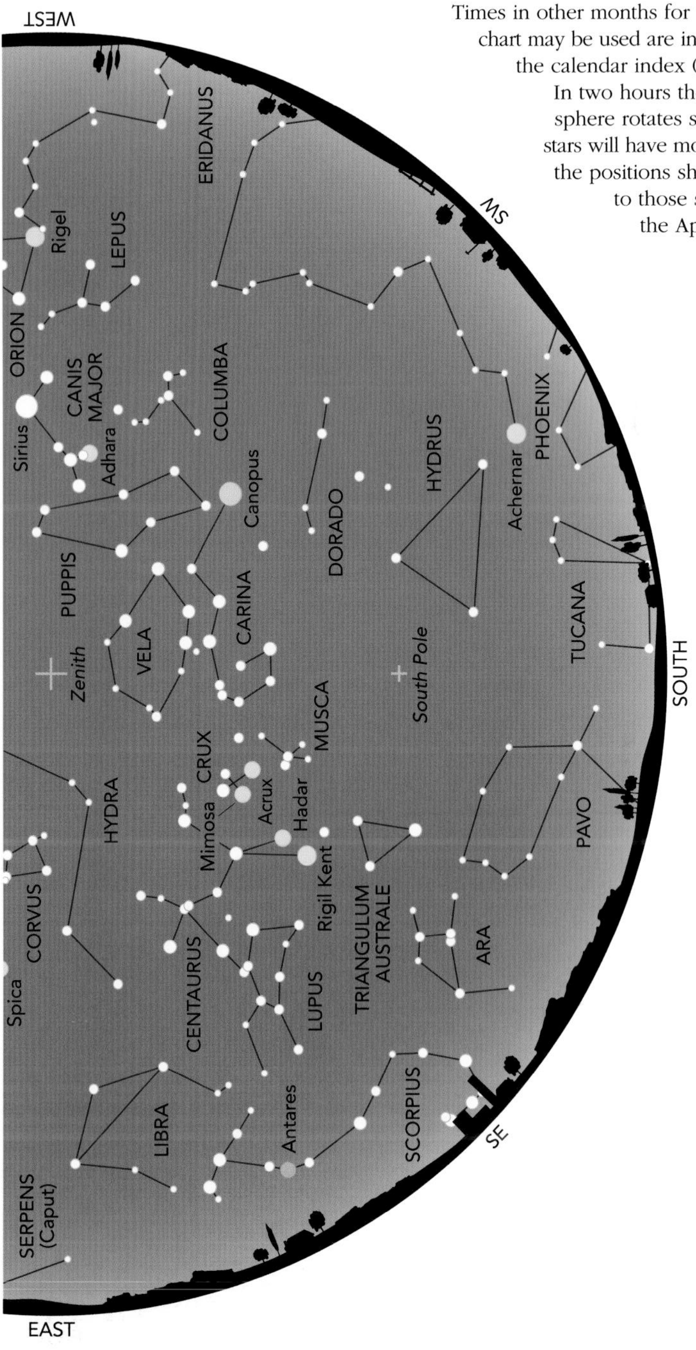

April – Looking North

The main constellations visible on April evenings. The positions are correct for 5 April at 11 p.m. and 20 April at 10 p.m. Use this pair of charts for other dates and times in April, for four minutes later each previous night, or four minutes earlier each following night: for example, 4 April at 11.04 p.m., 6 April at 10.56 p.m. or 10 April at 10.40 p.m.

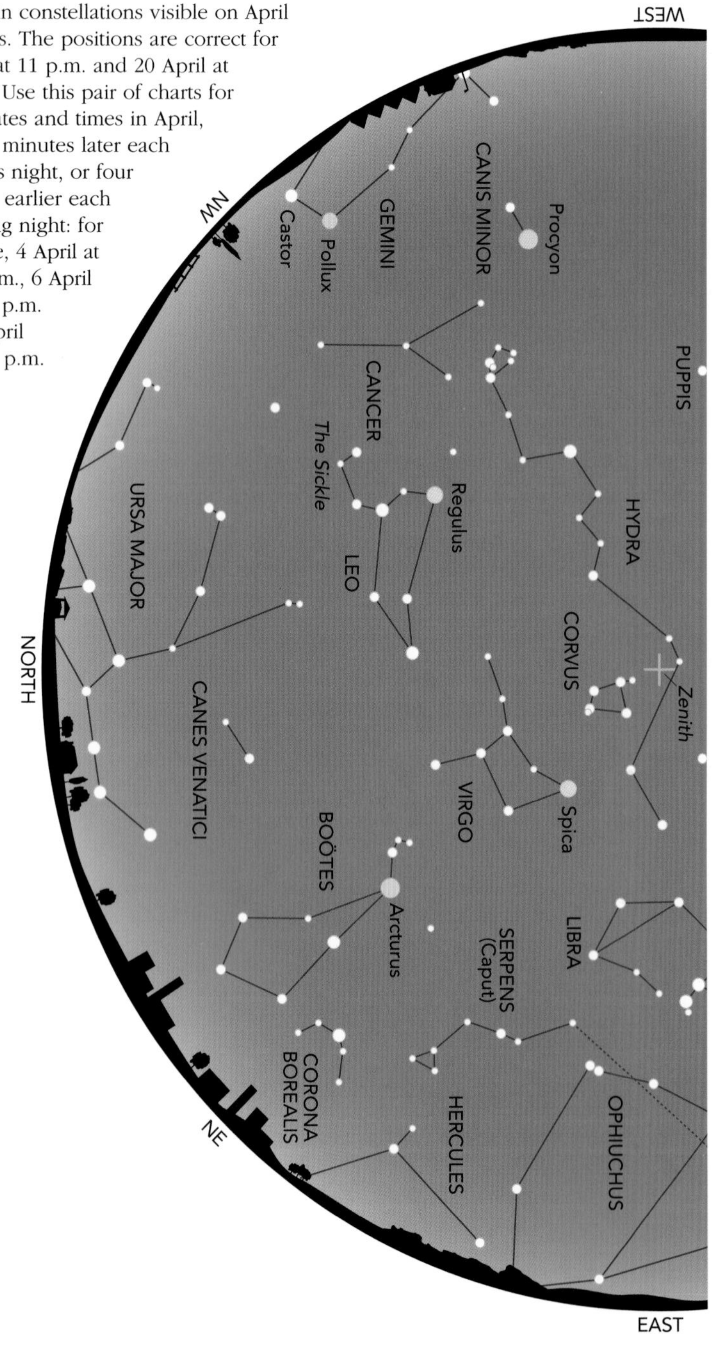

April – Looking South

Times in other months for which the chart may be used are indicated in the calendar index (page 12). In two hours the celestial sphere rotates so that the stars will have moved from the positions shown here to those shown on the May charts.

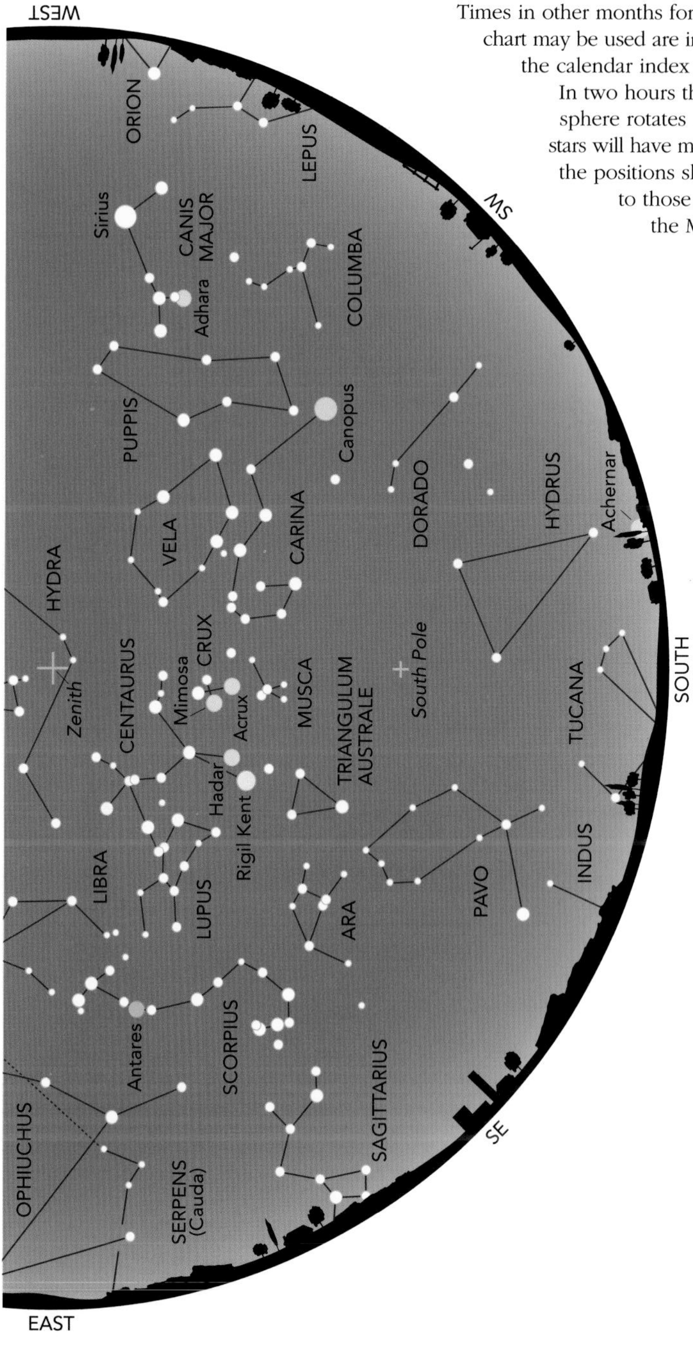

May – Looking North

The main constellations visible on May evenings. The positions are correct for 5 May at 11 p.m. and 20 May at 10 p.m. Use this pair of charts for other dates and times in May, for four minutes later each previous night, or four minutes earlier each following night: for example, 4 May at 11.04 p.m., 6 May at 10.56 p.m. or 10 May at 10.40 p.m.

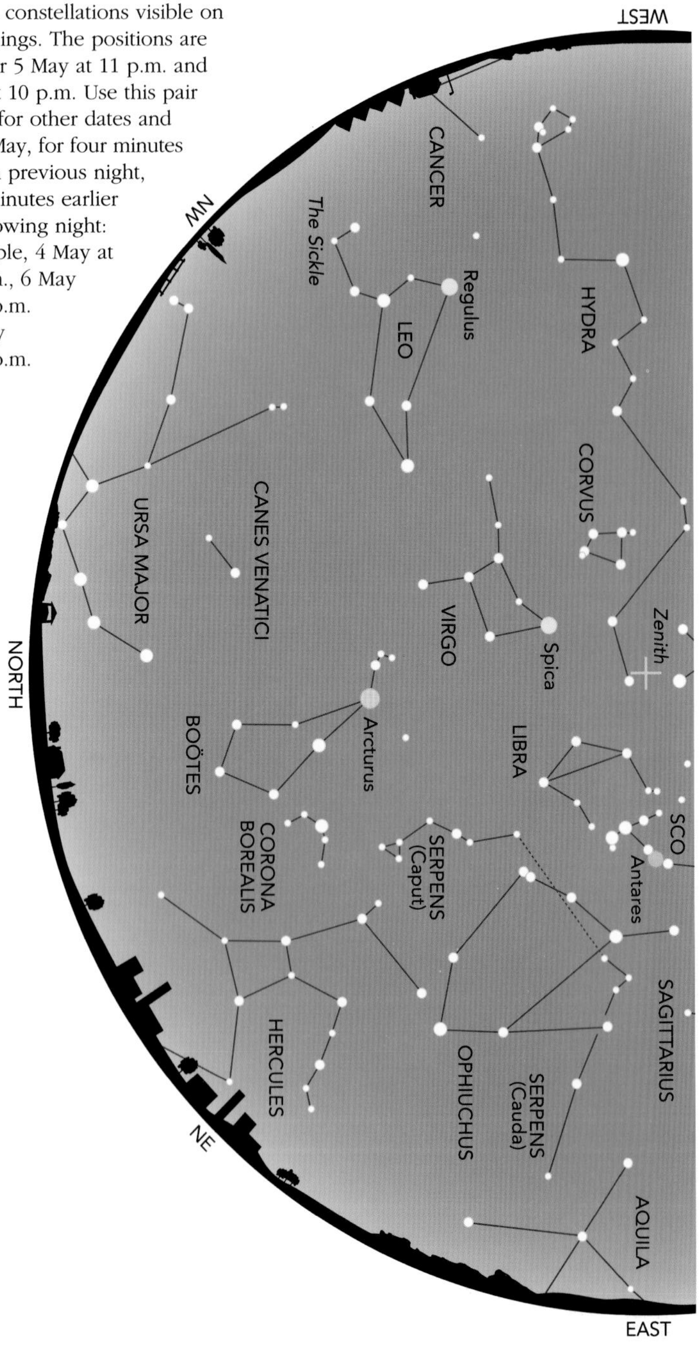

May – Looking South

Times in other months for which the chart may be used are indicated in the calendar index (page 12). In two hours the celestial sphere rotates so that the stars will have moved from the positions shown here to those shown on the June charts.

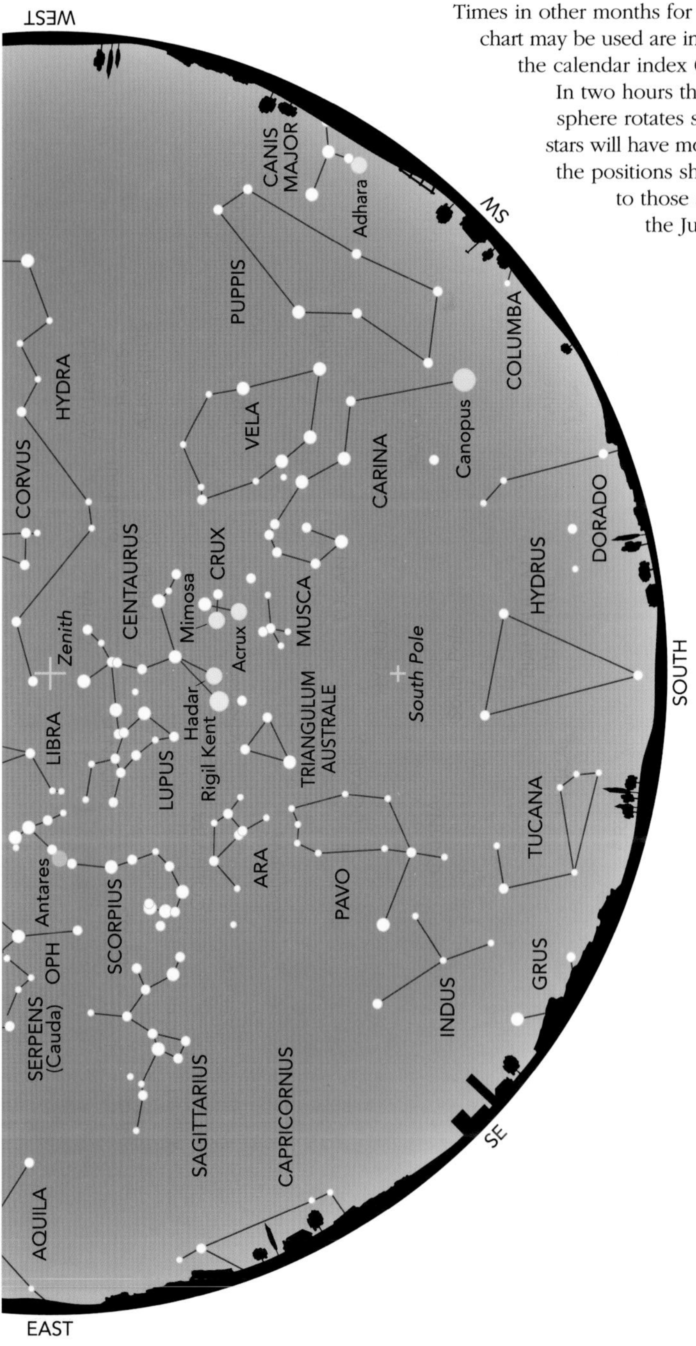

June – Looking North

The main constellations visible on June evenings. The positions are correct for 5 June at 11 p.m. and 20 June at 10 p.m. Use this pair of charts for other dates and times in June, for four minutes later each previous night, or four minutes earlier each following night: for example, 4 June at 11.04 p.m., 6 June at 10.56 p.m. or 10 June at 10.40 p.m.

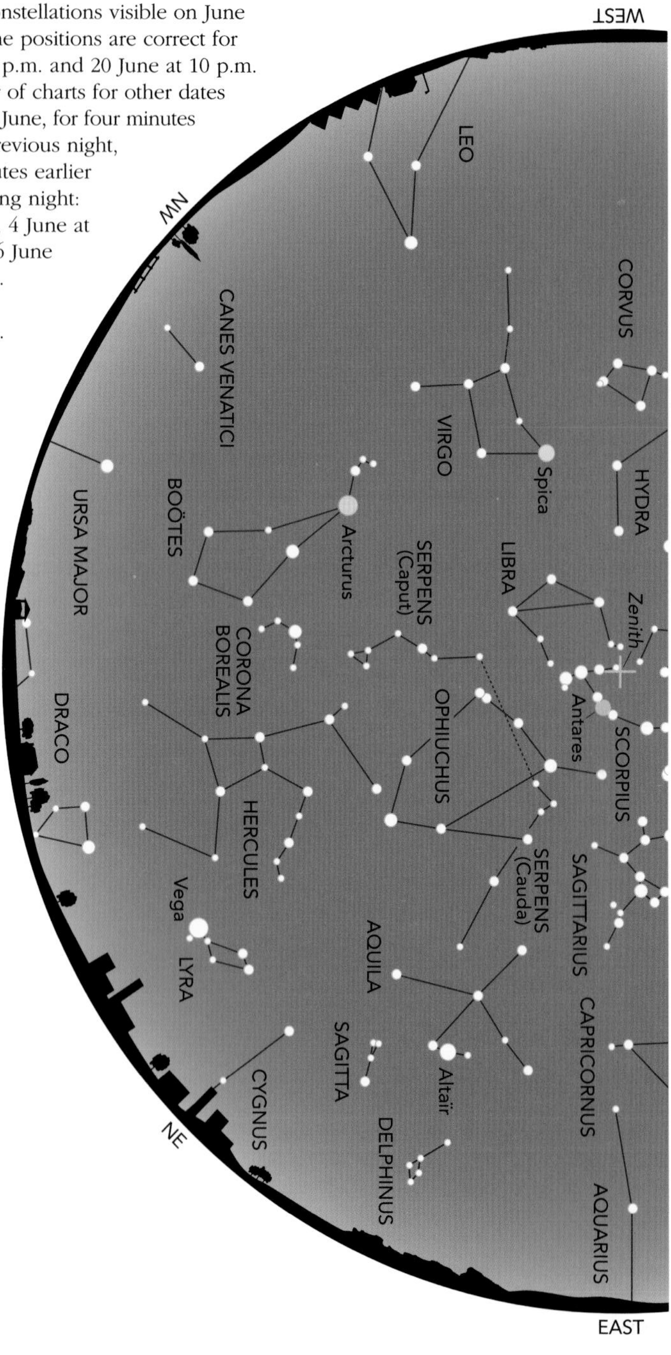

June – Looking South

Times in other months for which the chart may be used are indicated in the calendar index (page 12). In two hours the celestial sphere rotates so that the stars will have moved from the positions shown here to those shown on the July charts.

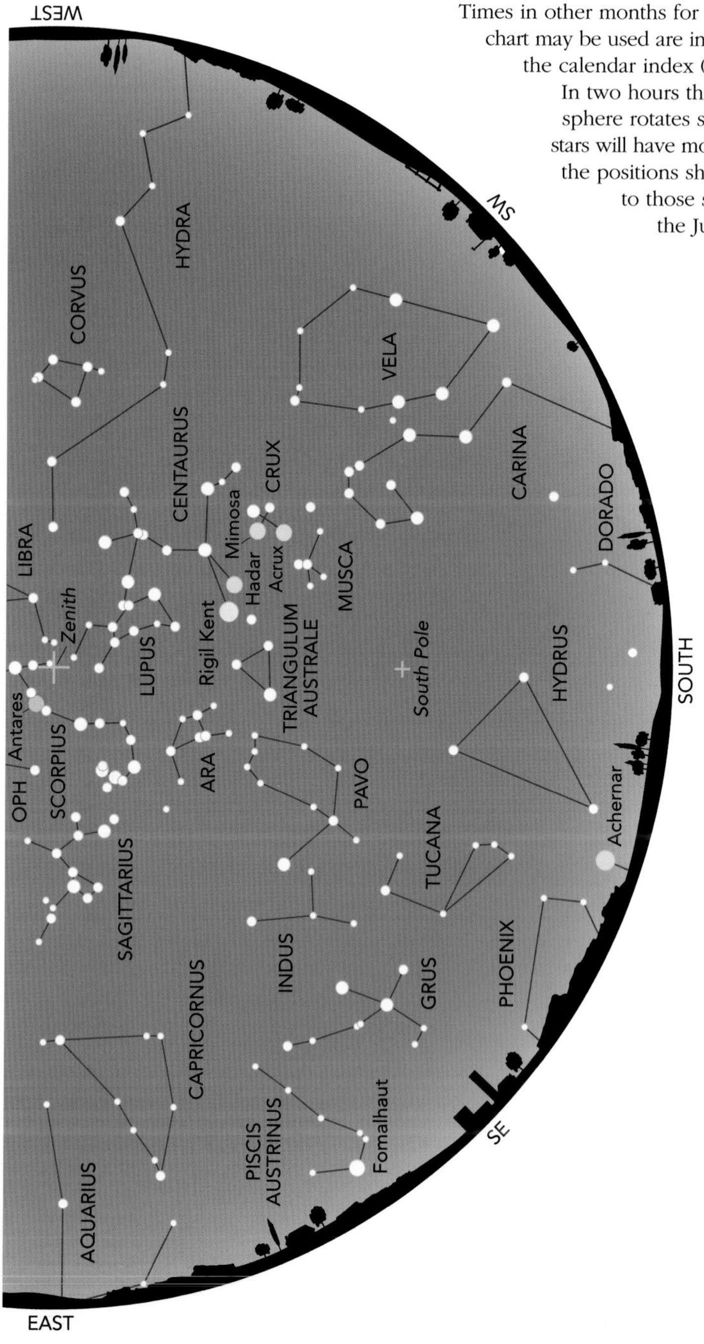

July – Looking North

The main constellations visible on July evenings. The positions are correct for 5 July at 11 p.m. and 20 July at 10 p.m. Use this pair of charts for other dates and times in July, for four minutes later each previous night, or four minutes earlier each following night: for example, 4 July at 11.04 p.m., 6 July at 10.56 p.m. or 10 July at 10.40 p.m.

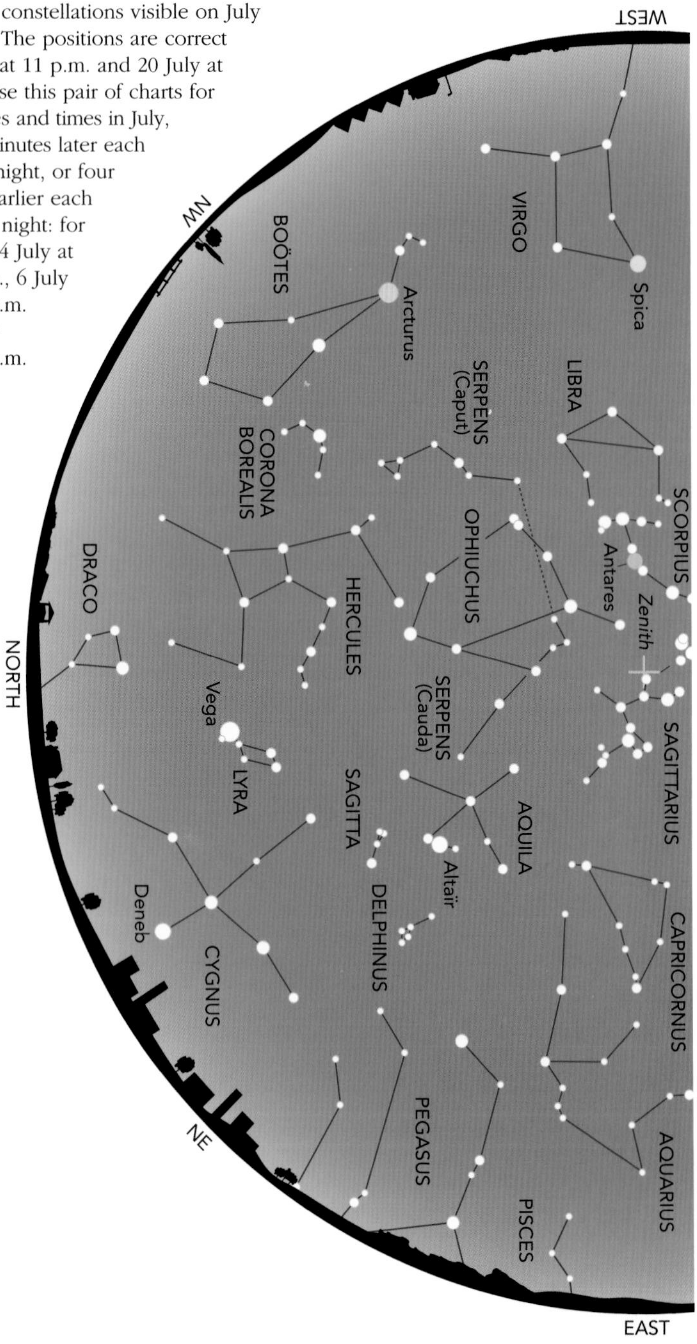

July – Looking South

Times in other months for which the chart may be used are indicated in the calendar index (page 12). In two hours the celestial sphere rotates so that the stars will have moved from the positions shown here to those shown on the August charts.

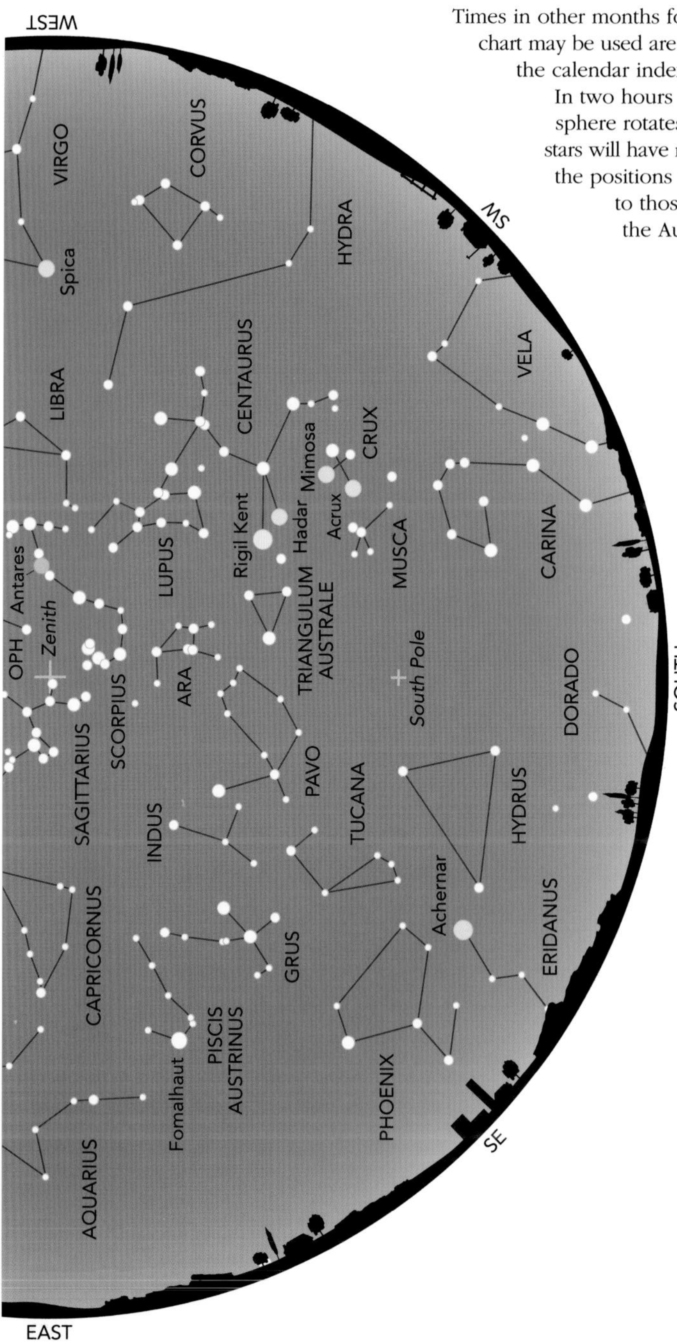

August – Looking North

The main constellations visible on August evenings. The positions are correct for 5 August at 11 p.m. and 20 August at 10 p.m. Use this pair of charts for other dates and times in August, for four minutes later each previous night, or four minutes earlier each following night: for example, 4 August at 11.04 p.m., 6 August at 10.56 p.m. or 10 August at 10.40 p.m.

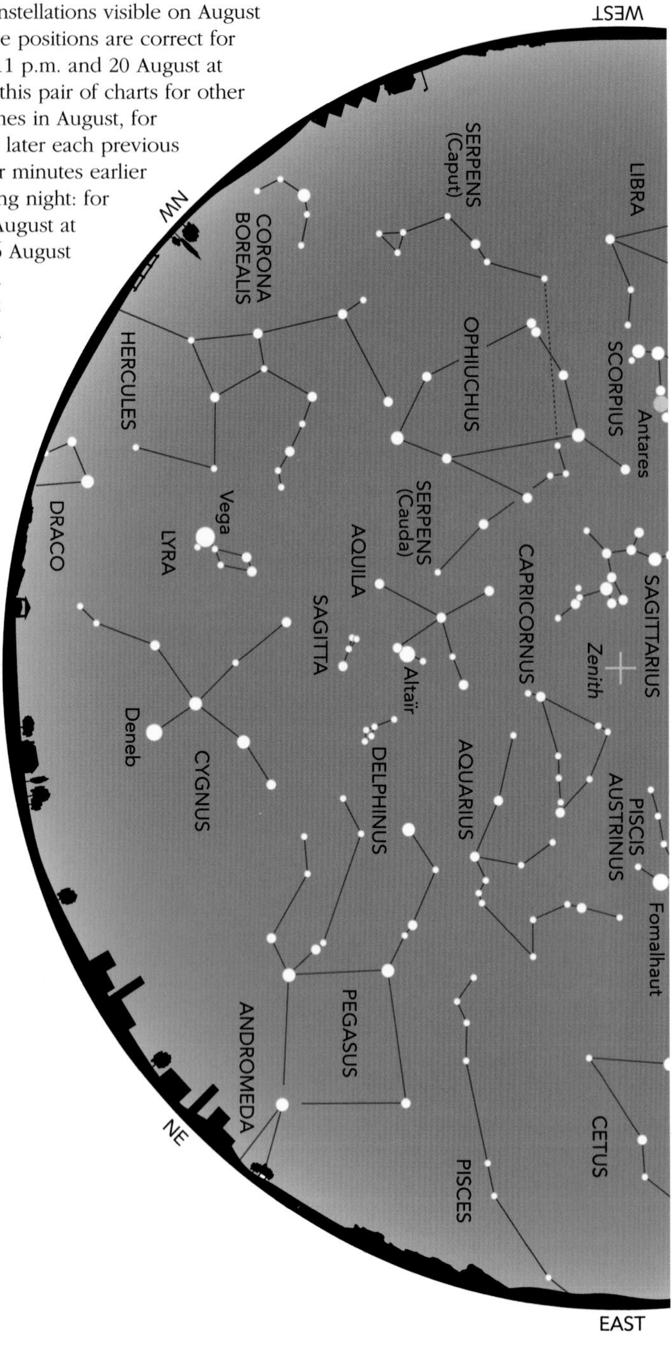

August – Looking South

Times in other months for which the chart may be used are indicated in the calendar index (page 12). In two hours the celestial sphere rotates so that the stars will have moved from the positions shown here to those shown on the September charts.

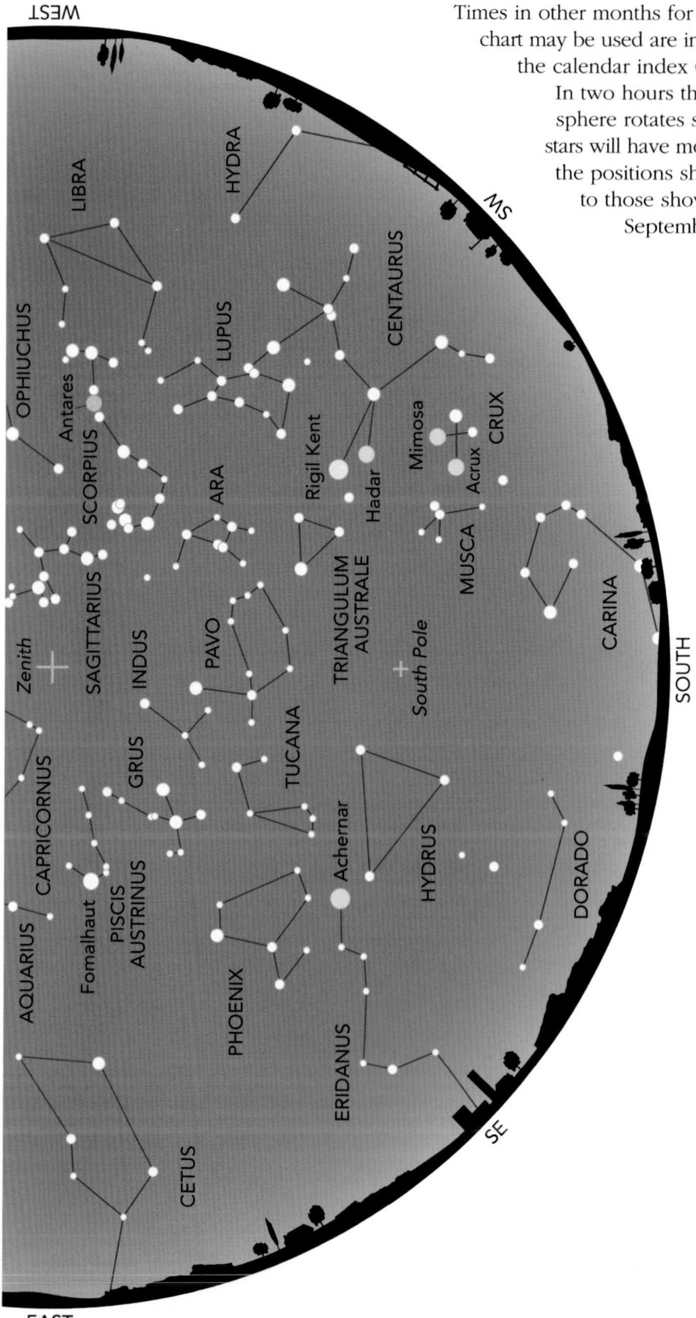

September – Looking North

The main constellations visible on September evenings. The positions are correct for 5 September at 11 p.m. and 20 September at 10 p.m. Use this pair of charts for other dates and times in September, for four minutes later each previous night, or four minutes earlier each following night: for example, 4 September at 11.04 p.m., 6 September at 10.56 p.m. or 10 September at 10.40 p.m.

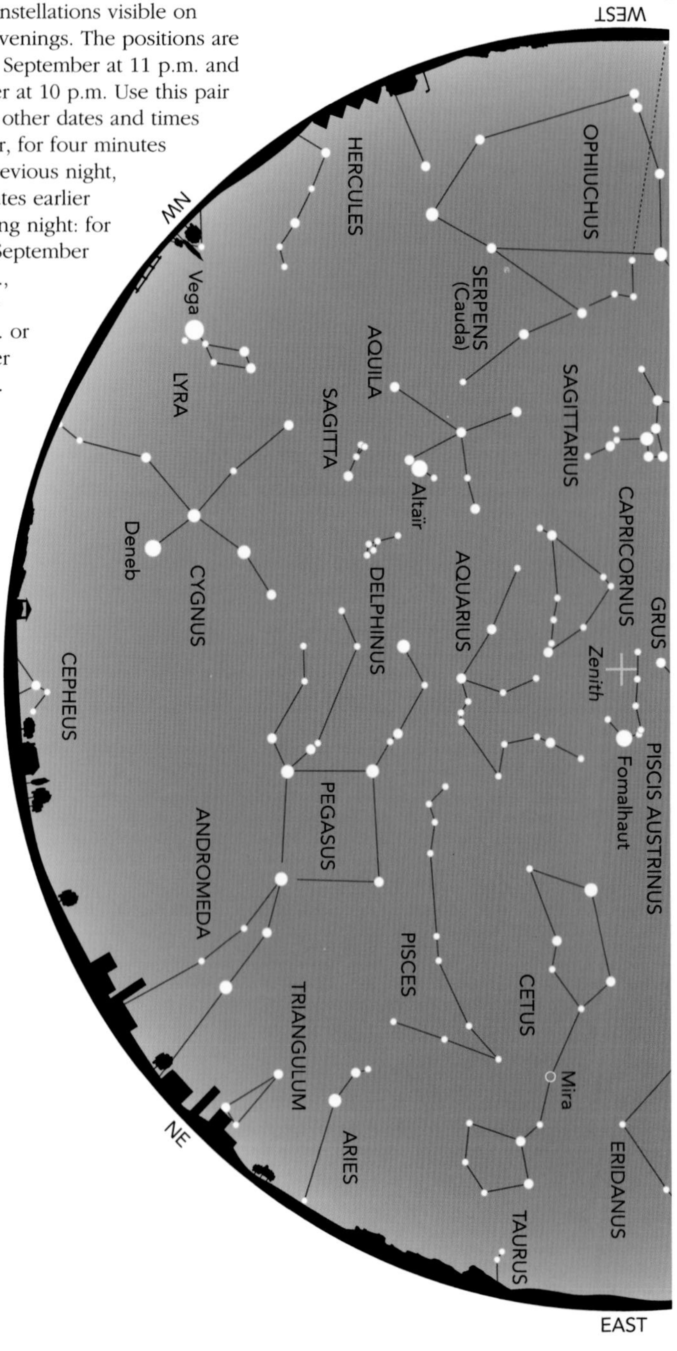

September – Looking South

Times in other months for which the chart may be used are indicated in the calendar index (page 12). In two hours the celestial sphere rotates so that the stars will have moved from the positions shown here to those shown on the October charts.

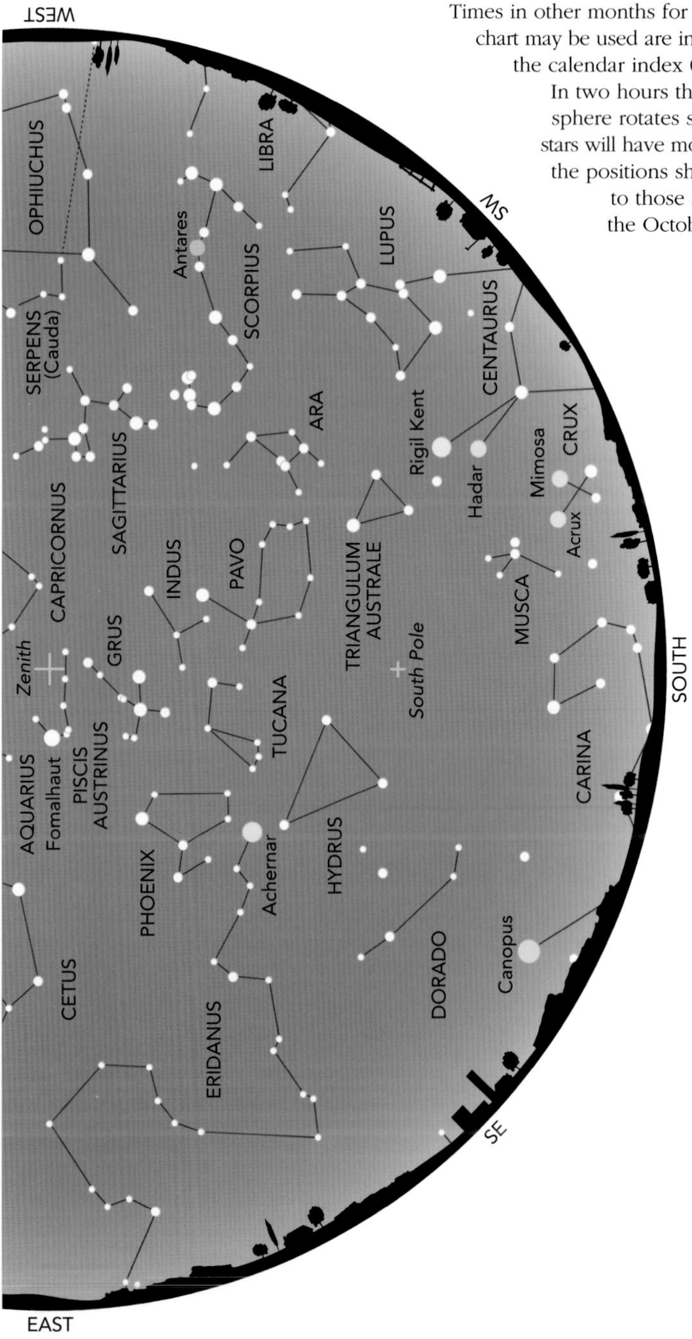

October – Looking North

The main constellations visible on October evenings. The positions are correct for 5 October at 11 p.m. and 20 October at 10 p.m. Use this pair of charts for other dates and times in October, for four minutes later each previous night, or four minutes earlier each following night: for example, 4 October at 11.04 p.m., 6 October at 10.56 p.m. or 10 October at 10.40 p.m.

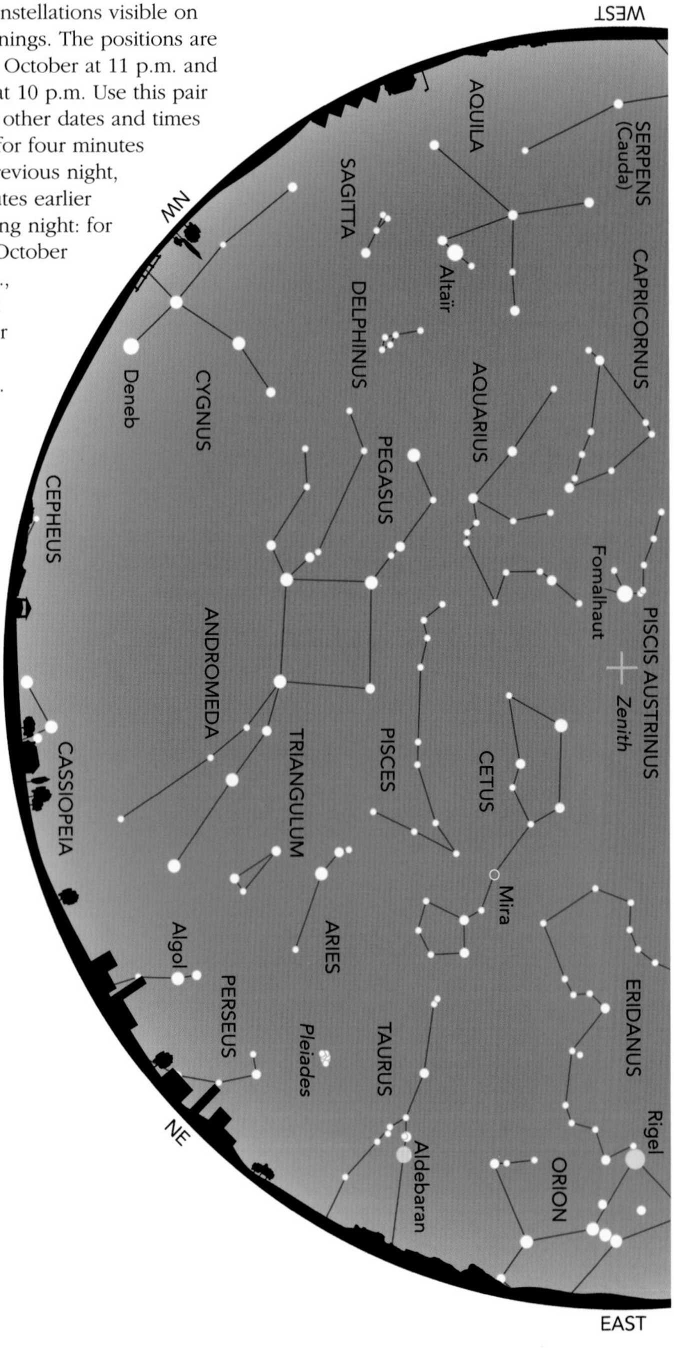

October – Looking South

Times in other months for which the chart may be used are indicated in the calendar index (page 12). In two hours the celestial sphere rotates so that the stars will have moved from the positions shown here to those shown on the November charts.

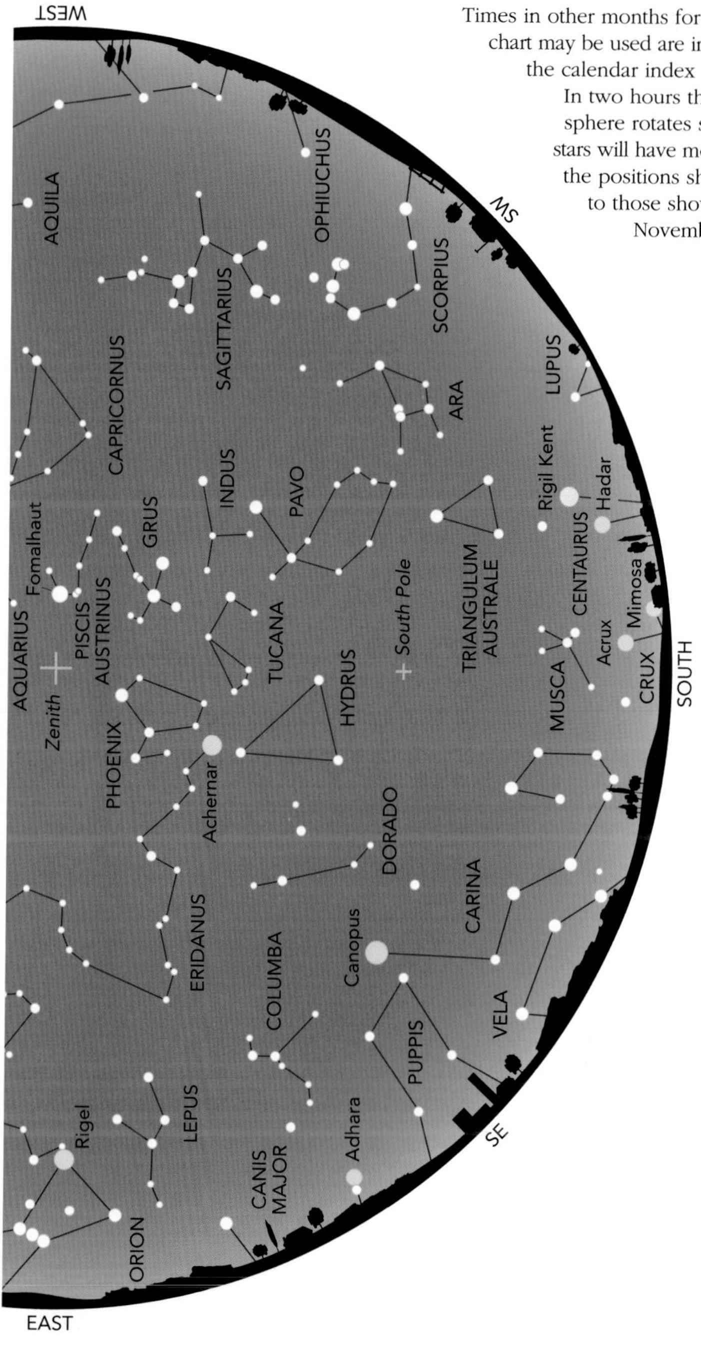

November – Looking North

The main constellations visible on November evenings. The positions are correct for 5 November at 11 p.m. and 20 November at 10 p.m. Use this pair of charts for other dates and times in November, for four minutes later each previous night, or four minutes earlier each following night: for example, 4 November at 11.04 p.m., 6 November at 10.56 p.m. or 10 November at 10.40 p.m.

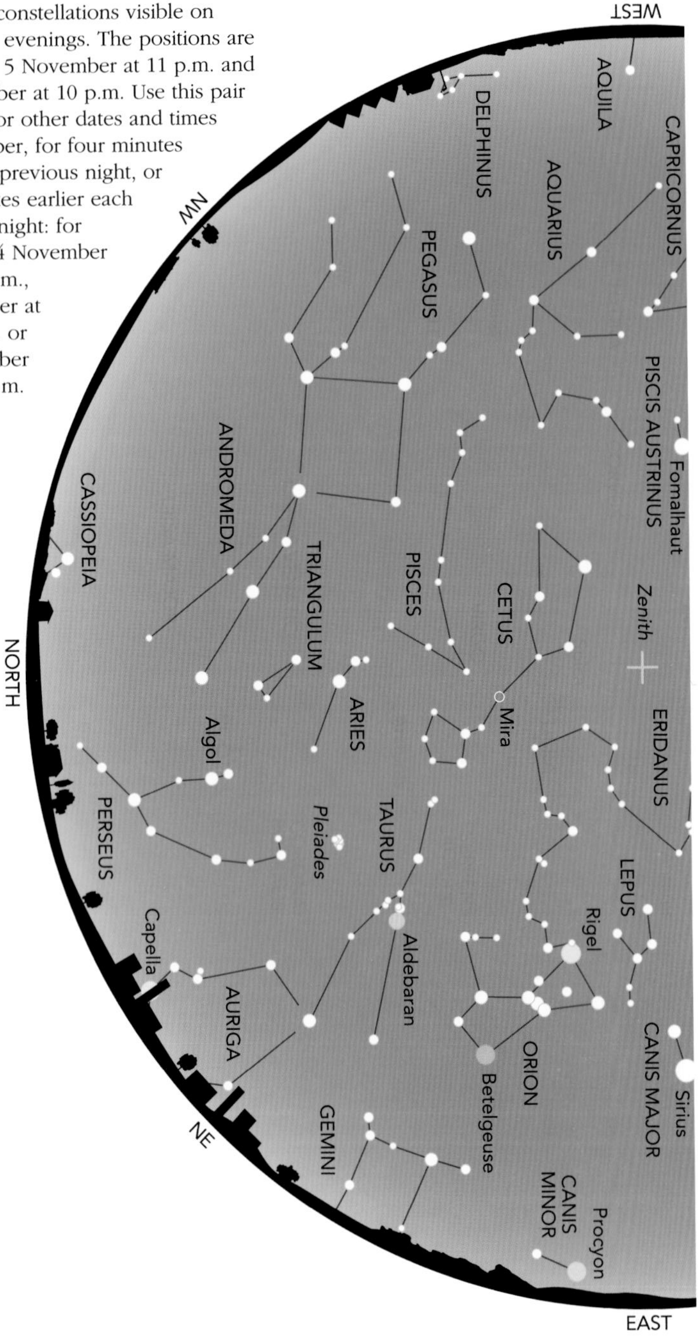

November – Looking South

Times in other months for which the chart may be used are indicated in the calendar index (page 12). In two hours the celestial sphere rotates so that the stars will have moved from the positions shown here to those shown on the December charts.

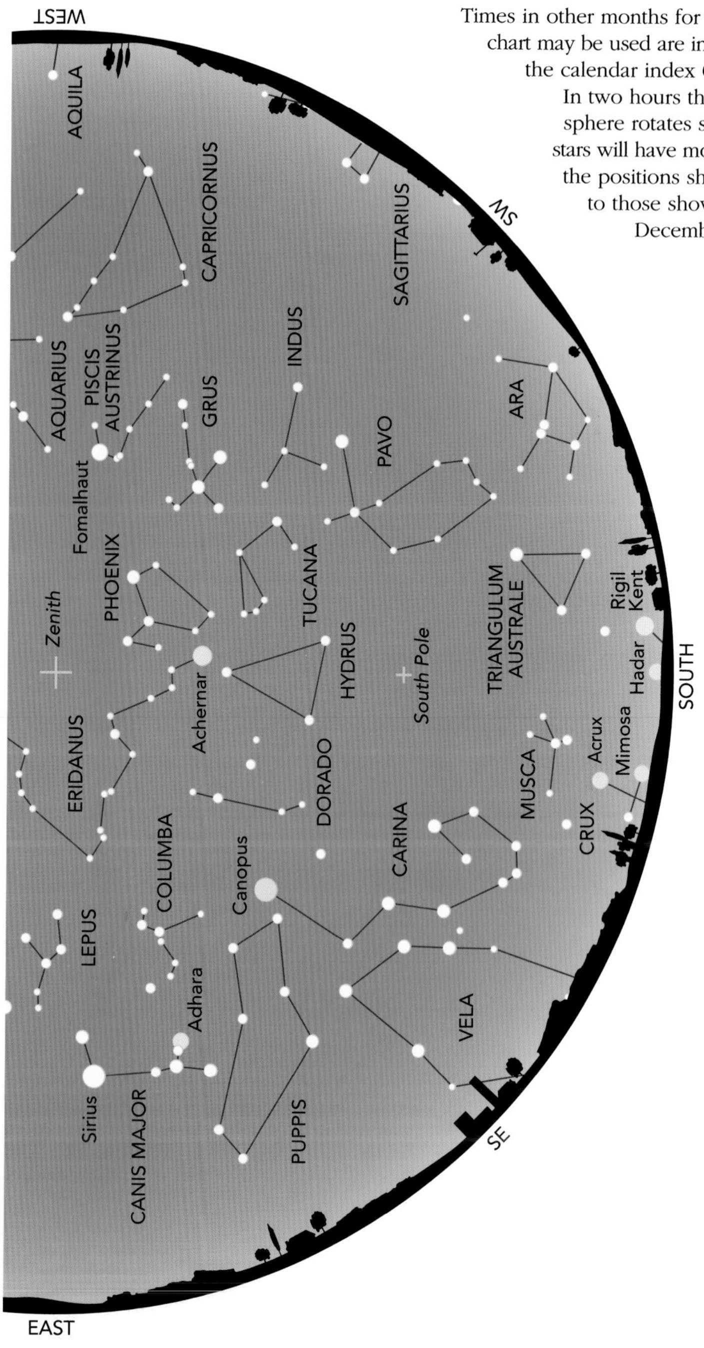

December – Looking North

The main constellations visible on December evenings. The positions are correct for 5 December at 11 p.m. and 20 December at 10 p.m. Use this pair of charts for other dates and times in December, for four minutes later each previous night, or four minutes earlier each following night: for example, 4 December at 11.04 p.m., 6 December at 10.56 p.m. or 10 December at 10.40 p.m.

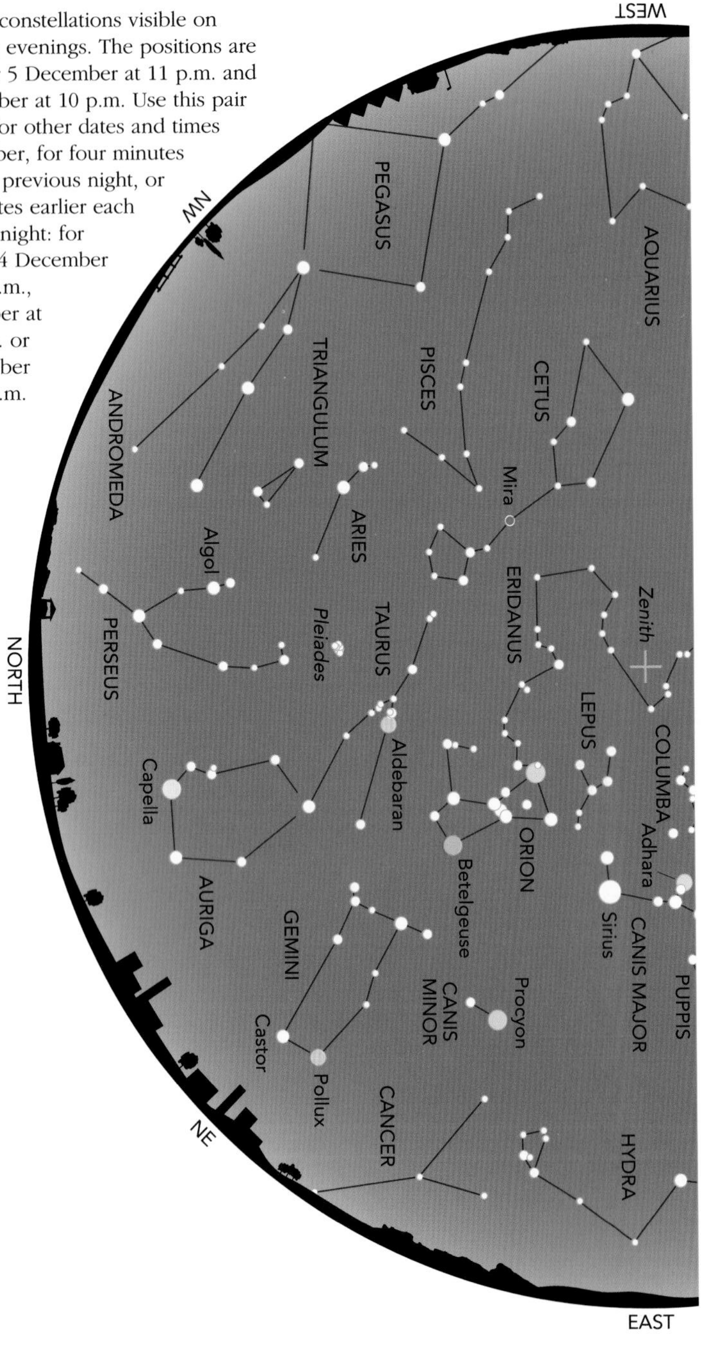

December – Looking South

Times in other months for which the chart may be used are indicated in the calendar index (page 12). In two hours the celestial sphere rotates so that the stars will have moved from the positions shown here to those shown on the January charts.

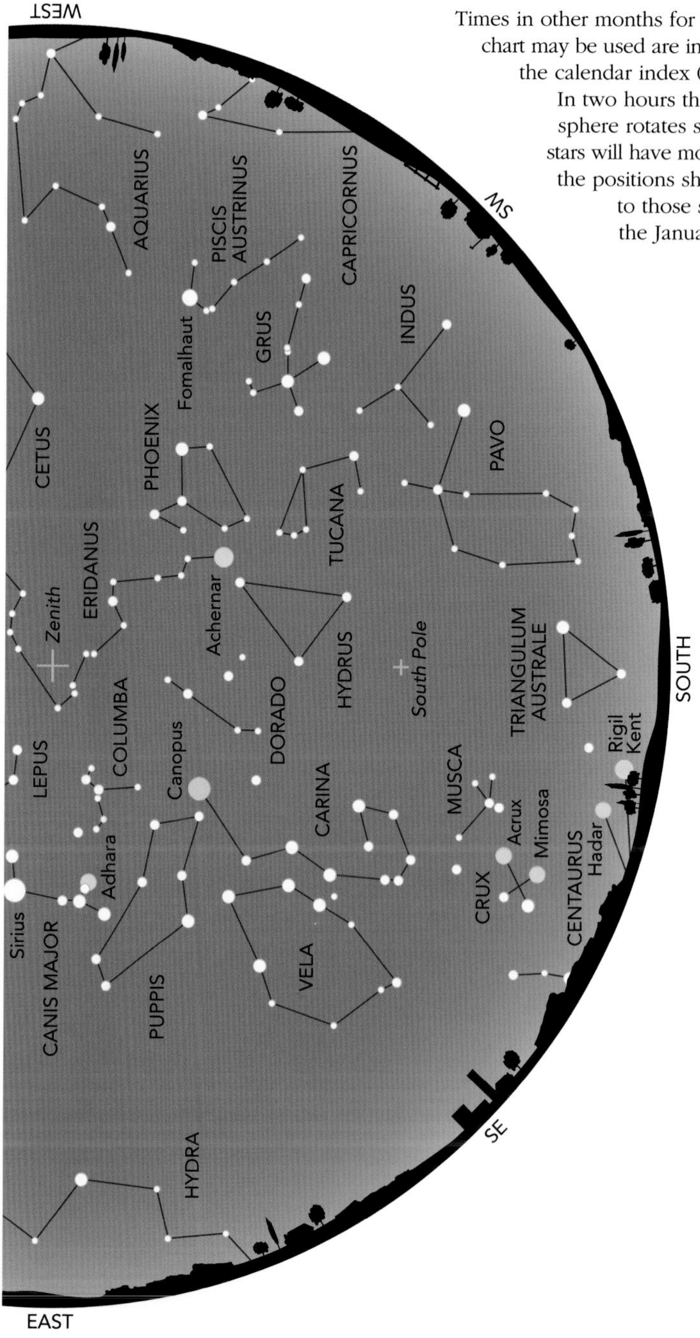

Constellations as Pointers

Some of the most prominent groups of stars are also the best celestial signposts.

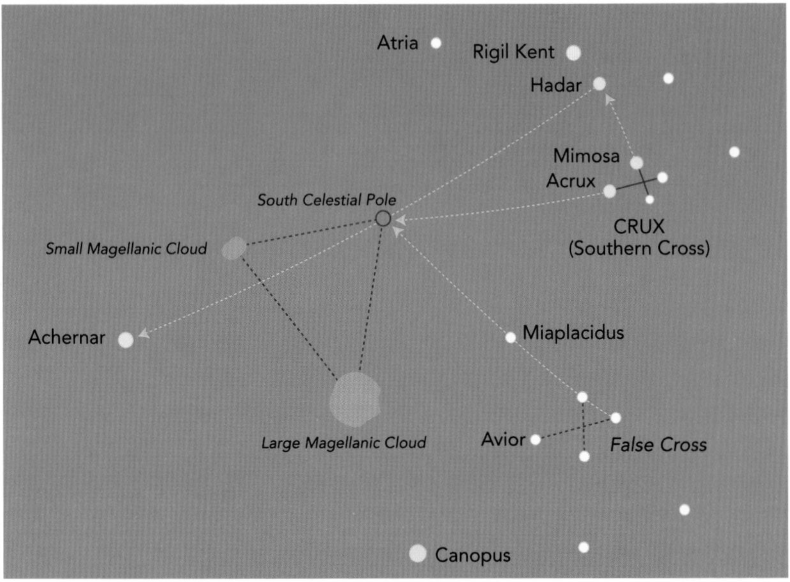

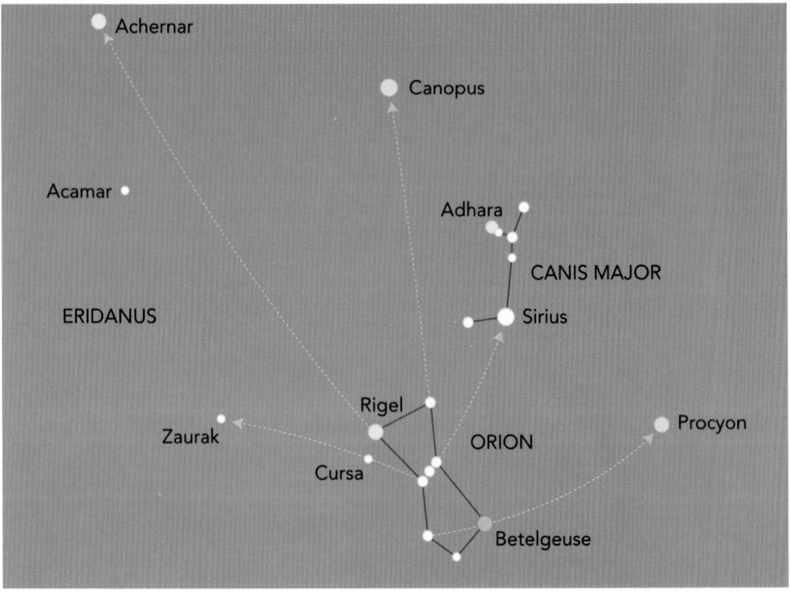

Make full use of these pointers when you start finding your way about the night sky.

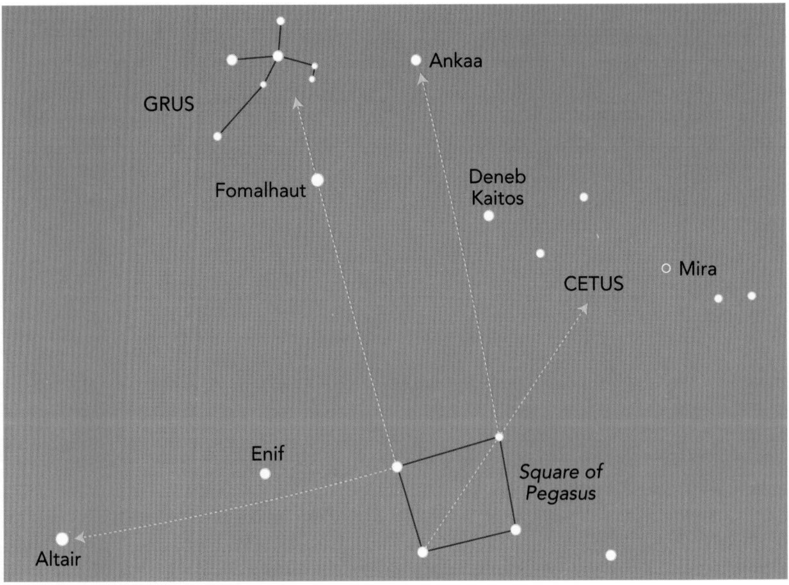

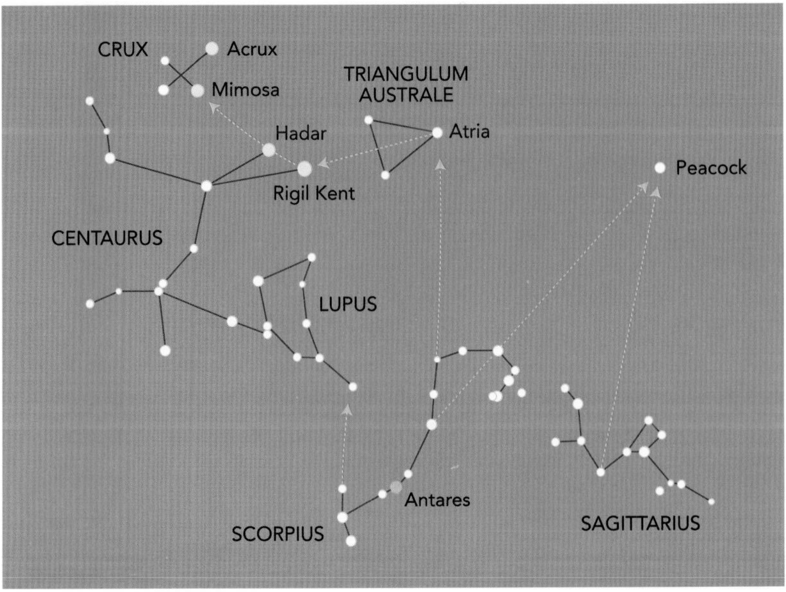

Finder Charts

These four pages show larger-scale charts which will help you to locate some of the best examples of different types of celestial object: a double star, a variable star, two star clusters, a globular cluster, a nebula and a galaxy. All but the galaxy can be seen with the naked eye, though binoculars or a small telescope will of course give better views.

Alpha Centauri, a double star

Many stars in the sky are *double stars*: binoculars or a telescope show not one star, but a pair. One of the most impressive examples is Alpha Centauri, comprised of two bright stars (magnitude 0.0 and +1.3) which orbit around a common centre of gravity once every 80 years. A small telescope or high-power binoculars will separate them. The brighter star is very similar to our own Sun, while the celebrated Proxima Centauri, a faint red dwarf which is the closest star to the Solar System, is also gravitationally connected.

A variable star: Mira

While most stars shine with a constant luminosity, others – called *variable stars* – fluctuate in their light output, often because they are pulsating. A famous example – one of the first variable stars to be discovered – is Mira in Cetus (Chart 5), which varies over a period of 330 days. At minimum, Mira is a tricky object in binoculars, but when at maximum light it is easily visible to the naked eye, usually peaking at third magnitude. The chart on the right shows the magnitudes of nearby stars for comparison. Brightness estimates made at intervals of a week or two will show how Mira's magnitude changes with time.

The Eta Carinae Nebula

Believed by many astronomers to be a supernova in waiting, the star Eta Carinae became unusually bright in the 19th cen-

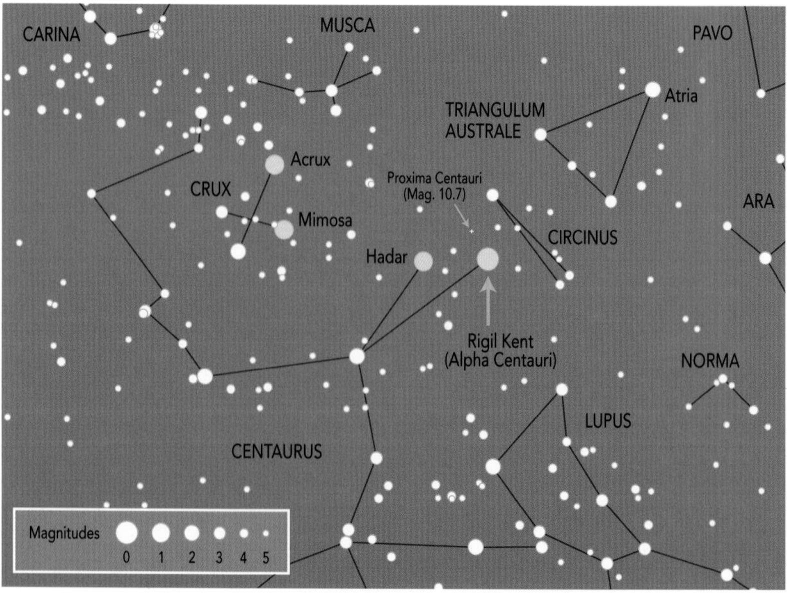

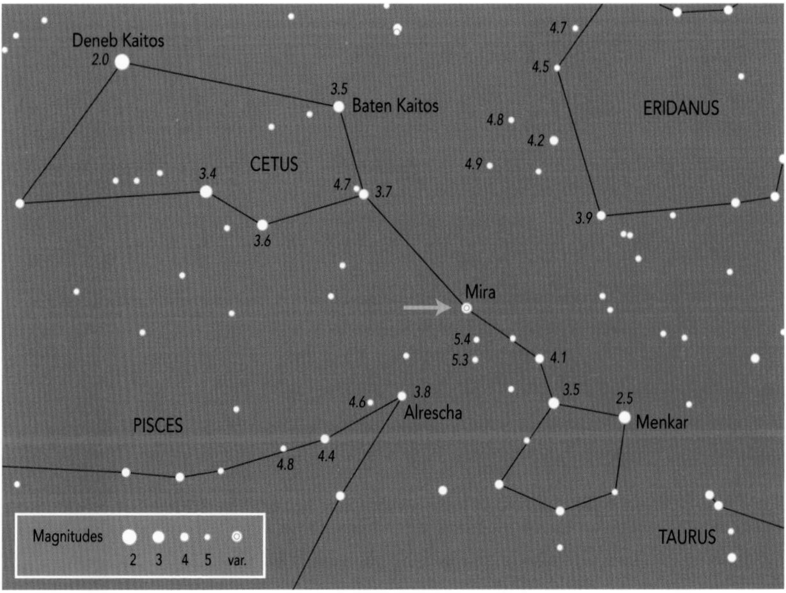
Deneb Kaitos
2.0
3.5
Baten Kaitos
CETUS
3.4
4.7
3.7
3.6
4.7
4.5
4.8
4.2
4.9
ERIDANUS
3.9
Mira
5.4
5.3
4.1
3.8
Alrescha
4.6
3.5
2.5
Menkar
PISCES
4.4
4.8
TAURUS
Magnitudes
2 3 4 5 var.

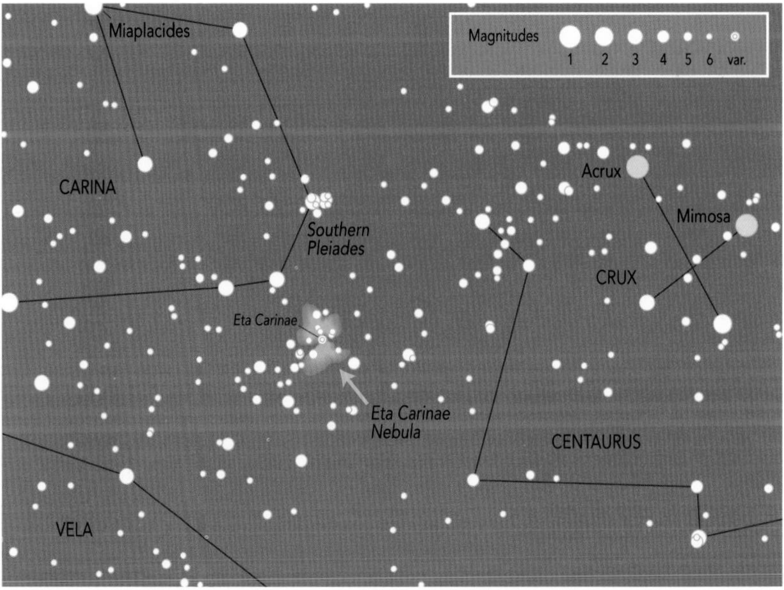
Miaplacides
Magnitudes
1 2 3 4 5 6 var.
CARINA
Acrux
Mimosa
Southern
Pleiades
CRUX
Eta Carinae
Eta Carinae
Nebula
CENTAURUS
VELA

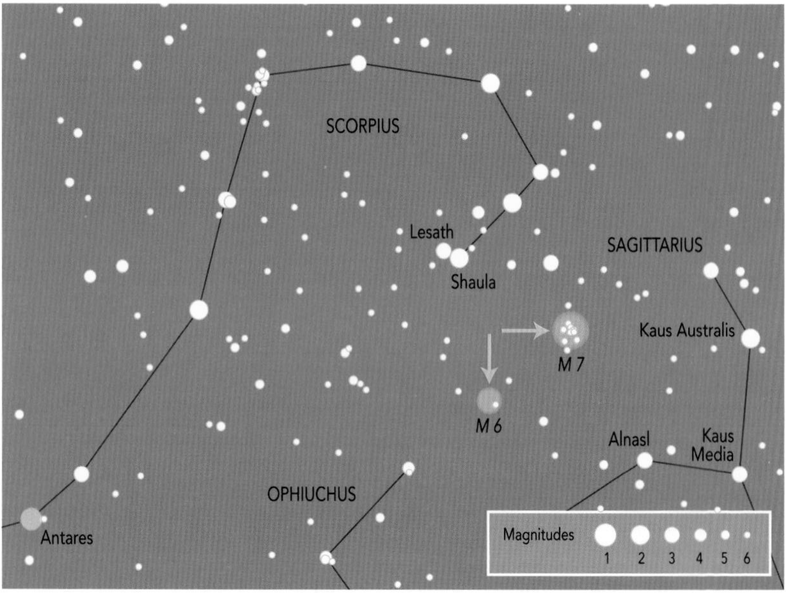

tury. It is surrounded by a bright cloud of gas and dust – a *nebula* ejected during past episodes of unusual activity. The Eta Carinae Nebula is one of the largest and brightest in the sky, with a diameter four times that of the Moon. Visible to the naked eye, the nebula shows a considerable amount of internal structure, including dark lanes and bright regions, and slowly changes over timescales of decades.

Star clusters: M6, M7 and Omega Centauri

Some stars reside not alone or in pairs, but in *star clusters*, groups that may have anything from a dozen to a million members. Two of the most striking examples in the southern sky are known by their catalogue numbers M6 and M7, and lie close to the Sting of Scorpius. Both are visible to the naked eye, with M7 being the brighter and more scattered. Binoculars reveal between 70 and 100 stars in each. Open clusters like M6 and M7 are usually young groupings of stars which have formed together. Rather different are objects like Omega Centauri (opposite), an ancient globular cluster containing hundreds of thousands of stars grouped together. Omega Centauri appears to the naked eye as a fourth-magnitude fuzzy 'star' (hence its stellar designation), but resolves into a grainy ball of stars with the slightest optical aid.

NGC 253 – The Silver Coin Galaxy

Our own Galaxy, which we see on a clear, dark night as the Milky Way, is but one of countless millions in the universe. Most of these, like NGC 253, require some optical aid to be seen. Binoculars will readily show this object in the otherwise undistinguished southern constellation of Sculptor. Also known as the Silver Coin from its photographic appearance, NGC 253 is one of the closer external galaxies to our own. Like the Milky Way, it is a spiral galaxy containing billions of stars, together with gas and dust.

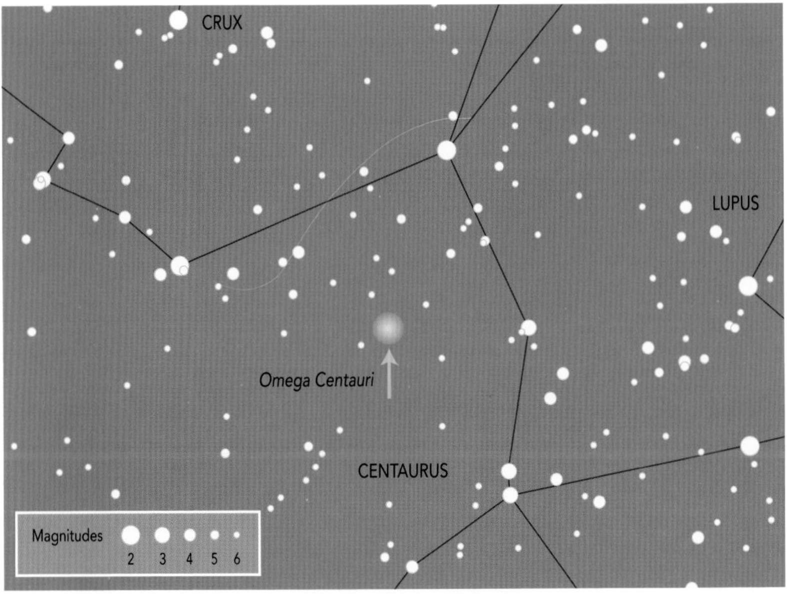
CRUX
LUPUS
Omega Centauri
CENTAURUS
Magnitudes
2 3 4 5 6

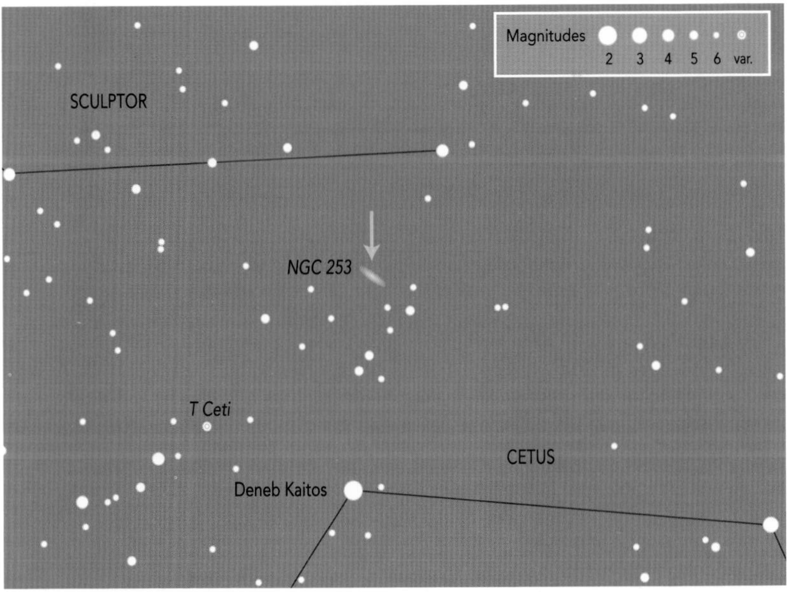
Magnitudes
2 3 4 5 6 var.
SCULPTOR
NGC 253
T Ceti
CETUS
Deneb Kaitos

Notes on the Constellations

The name of each constellation is followed by the number of the main chart(s) on which it is shown, together with its approximate position in right ascension (RA) and declination (dec), and the first monthly chart on which it appears (if no month is given, the constellation is either faint or in the far north). All the constellations are listed here, even the small ones that contain nothing of interest to the naked-eye observer. The most favourable times of year mentioned are when the particular constellation is highest in the sky in the late evening.

ANDROMEDA

Charts 3, 4, 6; RA 1h dec 40°; August

Andromeda's brightest stars, including the second-magnitude Mirach and Almaak, stretch away from the north-east corner of the Square of Pegasus. Alpheratz (also known as Sirrah), the star marking that corner, officially belongs to Andromeda rather than Pegasus. This constellation is most conspicuous in the spring and early summer, but is relatively low in the northern sky so that the famous Andromeda Galaxy (a naked-eye object for northern hemisphere observers) is not particularly well seen. This is the closest large galaxy beyond the Milky Way, and is the most distant object visible without a telescope or binoculars.

ANTLIA

Chart 5; RA 10h dec −30°

APUS

Chart 1; RA 15h dec −80°

AQUARIUS

Chart 3; RA 22h dec −10°; June

Aquarius lies between the Square of Pegasus and the bright star Fomalhaut, in Piscis Austrinus. This constellation, one of the 12 making up the zodiac, is one of the largest but contains no stars brighter than third magnitude. Aquarius is best placed for observation in the spring.

AQUILA

Chart 3; RA 20h dec 0°; May

Aquila lies in a rich part of the Milky Way, just north of the celestial equator. Its brightest star, the first-magnitude Altair, shines with a white radiance. Altair and the two fainter stars either side of it make a line which points towards Vega (in Lyra). Together with Deneb (in Cygnus), Vega and Altair form what northern observers call the Summer Triangle. At southerly latitudes, Altair and the rest of Aquila are best seen in the early spring.

ARA

Charts 1, 2, 3; RA 17h dec −50°

ARIES

Chart 4; RA 2h dec 20°; September

Aries is a rather insignificant constellation of the zodiac, and lies south of Andromeda. Its brightest star is the second-magnitude Hamal, which is midway between the Square of Pegasus and Aldebaran, in Taurus. Aries is best placed for observation in the early summer months.

AURIGA

Charts 4, 5, 6; RA 6h dec 40°; January

Auriga's brightest star is the intensely yellow, zero-magnitude Capella – the sixth-brightest star in the sky, and the third-brightest north of the celestial equator. Capella lies midway between

Orion and Polaris. Capella and the second-magnitude Menkalinan are circumpolar from the latitude of London. The constellation as a whole is best seen in January, low in the north. The second-magnitude star Elnath (sometimes spelt Al Nath), which may be considered part of the pattern of Auriga, belongs officially to Taurus, where it marks the tip of one of the Bull's horns.

BOÖTES

Charts 2, 6; RA 15h dec 30°; March

Boötes' leader is the strikingly orange zero-magnitude Arcturus, the brightest star in the northern celestial hemisphere, and the fourth-brightest of all the stars. Arcturus is prominent in the northern sky during the months of winter. Boötes also contains the second-magnitude Izar.

CAELUM

Charts 1, 4; RA 5h dec −40°

CAMELOPARDALIS

Charts 4, 6; RA 5h dec 60°

CANCER

Chart 5; RA 9h dec 20°; January

The faintest of the constellations of the zodiac, Cancer is bounded to the west by Castor and Pollux in Gemini, to the east by the Sickle of Leo, and to the south by the little group of stars representing the head of Hydra. Cancer is best placed for observation as summer gives way to autumn.

CANES VENATICI

Charts 2, 6; RA 13h dec 40°; March

A small constellation between the 'handle' of the Plough and Boötes. Its brightest star, named Cor Caroli, is only of third magnitude.

CANIS MAJOR

Chart 5; RA 7h dec −20°; January

A prominent constellation to the south-east of Orion, lying close to the Milky Way. It is dominated by the brilliant white Sirius (sometimes called the Dog Star), at magnitude −1.47 the brightest star in the sky, easily located by continuing the line of the three stars of Orion's belt (page 50). Canis Major is best seen in late January and early February when its southernmost stars, including Adhara, Wezen and Aludra, are overhead. With Procyon and Betelgeuse, Sirius makes up what is sometimes called the Winter Triangle by northern-hemisphere observers.

CANIS MINOR

Chart 5; RA 8h dec 10°; January

A small constellation close to the Milky Way east of Orion, in line with Bellatrix and Betelgeuse. Its brightest star is the pale yellow, first-magnitude Procyon which, with Betelgeuse and Sirius, forms the so-called Winter Triangle for observers in the northern hemisphere. February is the best time to see Canis Minor.

CAPRICORNUS

Chart 3; RA 21h dec −20°; June

A zodiacal constellation south of the celestial equator. Its brightest star, of third magnitude, lies about a third of the way along a line from Fomalhaut in Piscis Austrinus to Altair in Aquila; from there the constellation extends to the west and south-west. Capricornus is highest in the sky in September.

CARINA

Charts 1, 5; RA 6h to 11h, dec −60°

A southern circumpolar constellation whose brightest star, Canopus, lies midway between Sirius and the south celestial pole. The brilliant pale yellow Canopus, with a magnitude of −0.62, is the second-brightest star in the sky. From Canopus the rest of the constellation extends south-eastwards towards the Milky Way. Carina's other bright stars are Avior and Miaplacidus. Currently rather dim, but surrounded by an interesting nebula (pages 54–55), Eta Carinae brightened to rival Sirius in the 19th century, and may explode as a supernova in the distant future.

CASSIOPEIA

Charts 3, 4, 6; RA 1h dec 60°; October

Cassiopeia's five main stars form a very distinctive group resembling a slightly distorted letter W (or M, according to its orientation) drawn slantwise across the Milky Way, on the opposite side of Polaris from the Plough. The brightest of the five are the second-magnitude stars Schedar and Caph, forming the western end of the W. This northern circumpolar constellation barely clears the horizon on nights during the spring.

CENTAURUS

Charts 1, 2, 5; RA 13h dec −50°; January

Centaurus is a large southern circumpolar constellation. Its southern boundary lies along the Milky Way, where it all but surrounds the tiny but brilliant Crux. Here lie its two brightest stars, Rigil Kent and Hadar (with the alternative names Toliman and Agena, respectively). The orange-yellow Rigil Kent, also commonly known as Alpha Centauri, is the third-brightest star in the sky, with a magnitude of −0.28, and (with the exception of Proxima Centauri, a faint star visible only in telescopes) is also the closest star to the Earth, after the Sun. Alpha Centauri is a noted double star (page 52). First-magnitude Hadar is a blue-white star. The fourth-magnitude object designated Omega Centauri is not a star at all, but a globular cluster – a huge conglomeration of stars orbiting the Milky Way (pages 54–55). Centaurus is high in the sky during late autumn and early winter.

CEPHEUS

Charts 3, 6; RA 22h, dec 70°; September

A northern circumpolar constellation that occupies the triangular region bounded by Cassiopeia, Polaris and Deneb, in Cygnus. The southern part of Cepheus lies on the Milky Way; here are its brightest star, second-magnitude Alderamin, and the famous variable star Delta Cephei. Like neighbouring Cassiopeia, Cepheus barely clears the northern horizon during spring nights.

CETUS

Charts 3, 4; RA 2h dec −10°; August

A large constellation in the middle of what is often called the 'watery' part of the heavens: a large swathe of the night sky occupied by largely inconspicuous constellations with an aquatic theme. The brightest star in Cetus (the Whale), the second-magnitude Deneb Kaitos, has no nearby rivals and is easy to find. This constellation, best seen in the late autumn, contains the remarkable variable star Mira (pages 52–53). Mira can reach second magnitude, but at its faintest it is well below naked-eye visibility. A special symbol is used for it on the charts.

CHAMAELEON

Chart 1; RA 10h dec −70°

CIRCINUS

Charts 1, 2; RA 15h dec −60°

COLUMBA

Charts 1, 4, 5; RA 6h dec −40°; January

A small southern constellation whose brightest stars are of third magnitude.

Columba lies south of Orion and Lepus, and is overhead on summer nights.

COMA BERENICES

Charts 2, 5; RA 13h dec 20°

CORONA AUSTRALIS

Charts 1, 3; RA 19h dec −40°

CORONA BOREALIS

Chart 2; RA 16h dec 30°; April

A semicircle of stars between Boötes and Hercules, the brightest of which is the second-magnitude Alphekka. Corona Borealis is highest in the sky in mid-winter.

CORVUS

Charts 2, 5; RA 12h dec −20°; January

A small quadrilateral of stars to the south-west of Spica, in Virgo. Its brightest stars are of third magnitude. Corvus is best placed for observation in autumn, when it is high overhead.

CRATER

Charts 2, 5; RA 11h dec −20°

CRUX

Charts 1, 2, 5; RA 12h dec −60°; January

The smallest of all the constellations, but one of the most distinctive, this far-southern circumpolar group is popularly known as the Southern Cross. Its longer axis, marked by first-magnitude Acrux and second-magnitude Gacrux, points towards the south celestial pole (page 13). Acrux and first-magnitude Mimosa are distinctly blue. Next to Crux is what appears to be a gap in the Milky Way, devoid of stars: this is the Coalsack, a dark cloud of interstellar dust which blocks the light of stars beyond.

CYGNUS

Charts 3, 6; RA 20h dec 40°; June

Sometimes called the Northern Cross, Cygnus is best presented during the early spring, low in the north. The brightest star, Deneb (circumpolar from the latitude of London) is the most distant of all the first-magnitude stars. With Vega (in Lyra) and Altair (in Aquila), Deneb makes up northern observers' Summer Triangle. The long axis of the cross, marked by Deneb, second-magnitude Sadr and third-magnitude Albireo, stretches along the Milky Way. Albireo is a well-known double star, consisting of a third-magnitude yellow star with a fifth-magnitude blue companion.

DELPHINUS

Chart 3; RA 21h dec 20°; June

Delphinus is one of several small constellations in the region between Cygnus, Aquila and Pegasus, a compact group of fourth-magnitude stars that sparkles at the edge of the Milky Way on a clear night. The stars lie to the north-east of Altair, almost in line with the two upper stars of the Square of Pegasus. Delphinus is best placed for observation in the late winter.

DORADO

Charts 1, 4; RA 5h dec −60°; January

A small southern circumpolar constellation, about a third of the way along a line from Canopus, in Carina, to Achernar, in Eridanus. Its most notable feature is the Large Magellanic Cloud, one of two small galaxies in orbit around our own Galaxy, which we see as the Milky Way.

DRACO

Charts 2, 3, 6; RA 16h dec 60°; June

Draco is a northern circumpolar constellation that winds its way around Ursa Minor. Its brightest star is the second-magnitude Eltanin, one of the four stars marking the head of the Dragon, just to the north-west of Vega (in Lyra). From there the constellation snakes towards

Cepheus, then back in a curve of stars arcing around Kochab in Ursa Minor, and ending in a line of stars running across the top of the Plough. Only Draco's head is visible at southerly latitudes, in winter.

EQUULEUS

Chart 3; RA 21h dec 10°

ERIDANUS

Charts 1, 4; RA 4h dec 0° to −60°; January

Eridanus is one of the largest constellations. Representing a river, it begins with the first-magnitude blue-white star Achernar, then heads northwards, meandering back and forth until reaching its end just north-west of Rigel in Orion. Achernar is circumpolar at southerly latitudes, and the constellation as a whole is best viewed in late spring and early summer.

FORNAX

Chart 4; RA 3h dec −30°

GEMINI

Chart 5; RA 7h dec 20°; January

A bright constellation of the zodiac. Gemini's two brightest stars represent the legendary Twins: blue-white Castor is just below first magnitude, and the brighter, yellow Pollux is of first magnitude. These stars are easily found by starting from Orion (page 50). They are also due north of Procyon, in Canis Minor; to the north of them the sky is devoid of bright stars. The rest of the constellation, containing the second-magnitude Alhena, lies between Castor and Pollux and Orion. Gemini is best seen in January and February.

GRUS

Charts 1, 3; RA 23h dec −50°; January

A constellation to the immediate south of Piscis Austrinus. Its brightest star is the second-magnitude Alnair. Grus is often described, along with nearby Pavo, Tucana and Phoenix, as one of the 'Southern Birds'.

HERCULES

Charts 2, 3, 6; RA 17h dec 30°; April

One of the largest constellations, but not very conspicuous, Hercules contains no star brighter than third magnitude; the star Rasalgethi marks the giant's head. Hercules lies to the west of Lyra, and is best seen in the winter months.

HOROLOGIUM

Charts 1, 4; RA 3h dec −50°

HYDRA

Charts 2, 5; RA 8 to 15h dec −20°; January

The largest of all the constellations, representing a water snake, but by no means conspicuous. The creature's head is marked by a distinctive group of third- and fourth-magnitude stars due east of Procyon, in Canis Minor. South-east of the head is Hydra's brightest star, the second-magnitude Alphard. The rest of the constellation snakes eastwards, finishing up south of Virgo. As a whole, Hydra is best viewed in the early autumn.

HYDRUS

Chart 1; RA 2h dec −70°

INDUS

Charts 1, 3; RA 21h dec −50°

LACERTA

Chart 6; RA 22h dec 50°

LEO

Charts 2, 5; RA 11h dec 10°; January

A prominent constellation of the zodiac, Leo lies midway between the bright stars Arcturus, in Bootes, and Procyon, in Canis Minor. Its main feature is the distinctive Sickle asterism, resembling a reversed question mark. The 'dot' of the question mark is Leo's brightest star, the blue-white, first-magnitude Regulus. The Sickle also contains the second-magnitude Algieba. To the east of the Sickle is a triangle of stars, including second-magnitude Denebola. Leo is highest in the sky and best placed for observation in April.

LEO MINOR
Chart 5; RA 10h dec 30°

LEPUS
Chart 4; RA 5h dec −20°; January
A small group of stars, none brighter than third magnitude, immediately south of Orion. Lepus is best placed for viewing in January, when it is almost overhead.

LIBRA
Chart 2; RA 15h dec −20°; March
A constellation of the zodiac located between Scorpius and Virgo; none of its stars is brighter than third magnitude. In ancient times, its stars were used to mark Scorpius' claws. The best time for viewing Libra is midwinter.

LUPUS
Charts 1, 2; RA 15h dec −40°
A southern circumpolar constellation to the south-west of Scorpius, running along the edge of the Milky Way. The brightest star is of second magnitude, but Lupus is quite conspicuous on a clear night as it contains quite a high concentration of stars of third and fourth magnitude. Many of Lupus' stars are young and very luminous. The constellation is best seen in winter.

LYNX
Charts 5, 6; RA 8h dec 50°

LYRA
Charts 3, 6; RA 19h dec 40°; June
Lyra lies just off the northern Milky Way. At magnitude zero, its brightest star, Vega, is the second-brightest in the northern hemisphere, and the fifth-brightest in the whole sky. The brilliant blue-white Vega is low to the north on winter nights. With Deneb, in Cygnus, and Altair, in Aquila, it makes up the northern observers' Summer Triangle.

MENSA
Chart 1; RA 6h dec −80°
The faintest of all the constellations, located near the south celestial pole and therefore never setting at the latitude of Sydney. Its only distinction is that it contains part of the Large Magellanic Cloud, one of two small galaxies in orbit around our own Galaxy, which we see as the Milky Way.

MICROSCOPIUM
Charts 1, 3; RA 21h dec −40°

MONOCEROS
Chart 5; RA 7h dec 0°

MUSCA
Chart 1; RA 13h dec −70°

NORMA
Charts 1, 2; RA 16h dec −50°

OCTANS
Chart 1; RA 20h dec −80°
This otherwise unremarkable constellation contains the south celestial pole.

OPHIUCHUS
Chart 2; RA 17h dec −10°; April
A large but not prominent constellation which crosses the celestial equator and lies between Hercules and Scorpius. Although it is not one of the 12 constella-

tions of the traditional zodiac, the ecliptic does pass through it, so planets are sometimes found here. The brightest stars are second-magnitude Rasalhague and Sabik. July is the best time to see Ophiuchus.

ORION

Charts 4, 5; RA 6h dec 0°

The most brilliant of all the constellations – an unmistakable feature of the summer skies and the chief guide to the other constellations on view in the summer months (page 50). Rigel's pale blue radiance is set off by the striking red of Betelgeuse (occasionally spelt Betelgeux); these two first-magnitude stars lie at opposite corners of the constellation's main rectangular pattern. The other two corners are formed by second-magnitude Bellatrix and Saiph. At the centre of the rectangle are the three stars that comprise what is known as Orion's Belt: Alnitak, Alnilam and Mintaka, all of second magnitude. Mintaka lies very close to the celestial equator. South of the Belt is the Orion Nebula, a vast cloud of gas and dust visible to the naked eye as a faint, misty patch. The constellation is highest in the sky in January.

PAVO

Charts 1, 3; RA 20h dec −70°; January

A southern circumpolar constellation lying between Sagittarius and the south celestial pole, whose brightest star, known as Peacock, is of second magnitude.

PEGASUS

Charts 3, 4; RA 23h dec 20°; July

A large constellation best known for the Square of Pegasus: four stars that make up a near-perfect square which is a feature of the skies of late winter, spring and early summer. The Square provides a useful means of locating other constellations (page 50). The four stars of the square are Alpheratz (which officially belongs to Andromeda), Scheat, Markab and Algenib, all second magnitude apart from Algenib, which is third magnitude. From the Square, the rest of the constellation, including second-magnitude Enif, extends to the west towards Aquila. A line traced from Algenib through Alpheratz roughly indicates the zero line from which right ascension is measured.

PERSEUS

Charts 4, 6; RA 4h dec 40°; January

Perseus lies between Capella, in Auriga, and Andromeda. Its stars are low in the north, just below the Pleiades in Taurus, during summer nights. and north of the Pleiades, in Taurus. Second-magnitude Mirfak is the brightest star, and Algol is a well-known variable star, fluctuating between second and third magnitude. Perseus lies on the Milky Way.

PHOENIX

Charts 1, 3, 4; RA 1h dec −50°; January

A southern constellation that lies between Achernar, in Eridanus, and Fomalhaut, in Piscis Austrinus. Its brightest star is the second-magnitude Ankaa. Phoenix is highest during late spring nights.

PICTOR

Charts 1, 4, 5; RA 6h dec −60°

PISCES

Charts 3, 4; RA 1h dec 10°; July

Pisces is a large constellation, one of the 12 that make up the zodiac, but is quite inconspicuous, containing no star brighter than fourth magnitude. It occupies the area to the east and south of the Square of Pegasus, in the 'watery' region of the sky: Cetus (the Whale) lies to its south, and Aquarius to the west. Pisces is best seen in November.

PISCIS AUSTRINUS

Chart 3; RA 22h dec −30°; June

A constellation whose brightest star, first-magnitude Fomalhaut, is located by extending a line southwards from the western edge of the Square of Pegasus (page 50). Fomalhaut has no bright stars close to it.

PUPPIS

Charts 1, 5; RA 8h dec −40°; January

Puppis occupies the region between and to the east of Canis Major and Canopus, in Carina, extending towards the Milky Way. Puppis is in the zenith during summer nights.

PYXIS

Chart 5; RA 9h dec −30°

RETICULUM

Charts 1, 4; RA 4h dec −60°

SAGITTA

Chart 3; RA 20h dec 20°; June

A faint but distinctive arrow-shaped formation of stars in the Milky Way just north of Altair, in Aquila. Sagitta is highest in the sky in the late summer.

SAGITTARIUS

Charts 1, 2, 3; RA 19h dec −30°; April

A bright constellation of the zodiac, situated in the Milky Way to the east of Scorpius and south of Aquila. Its northern part contains its brightest stars, including the second-magnitude Nunki and Kaus Australis. The centre of our home Galaxy is located in Sagittarius, and the line of sight towards it takes in many rich starfields and clusters. Sagittarius is high overhead in late summer.

SCORPIUS

Charts 1, 2; RA 17h dec −30°; March

A conspicuous and distinctively shaped constellation of the zodiac, lying in the Milky Way to the west of Sagittarius. The constellation's brightest stars are orange-red first-magnitude Antares, and Graffias, just below second magnitude. The southern stars, making up the Scorpion's sting, include Shaula, one of the brightest of all second-magnitude stars. Like its neighbour Sagittarius, Scorpius abounds with rich starfields and clusters. Scorpius is best seen on nights in June and July, when it is close to the zenith.

SCULPTOR

Charts 3, 4; RA 0h dec −30°

SCUTUM

Chart 3; RA 19h dec −10°

SERPENS

Charts 2, 3; RA 18h dec −10° (Cauda) / RA 16h 10° (Caput); April/May

This constellation has the distinction of being the only one that is split into two sections. The western part, between Ophiuchus and Arcturus, in Boötes, represents the serpent's head and is often referred to as Serpens Caput. Its tail, Serpens Cauda, lies between Ophiuchus and Aquila. Its brightest stars are of third magnitude. Serpens is best viewed in the winter months.

SEXTANS

Chart 5; RA 10h dec 0°

TAURUS

Chart 4; RA 4h dec 20°

A prominent constellation of the zodiac, lying between Orion and Perseus, just off the Milky Way. Its brightest star is the first-magnitude, orange-red Aldebaran, found by following the line of Orion's Belt to the north. The second-brightest is Elnath, midway between Betelgeuse, in Orion, and Capella, in Auriga. The line from Orion's Belt to Aldebaran continues to the Pleiades, a prominent star cluster with six members visible to the naked eye, more on clear nights. Behind Aldebaran is another star cluster, the Hyades, whose members are rather more scattered; the brightest form a distinctive V-shape. Taurus is highest in the sky and best placed for observation in December and January.

TELESCOPIUM
Charts 1, 3; RA 19h dec −50°

TRIANGULUM
Chart 4; RA 2h dec 30°; September
A small constellation just to the south-east of Almaak and Mirach, in Andromeda. Its brightest stars are of third magnitude. Triangulum is best seen at the end of November.

TRIANGULUM AUSTRALE
Chart 1; RA 16h dec −70°
A southern circumpolar constellation in the Milky Way to the south-east of Rigil Kent, in Centaurus, and rather more prominent than its northern namesake. Its brightest star, of second magnitude, is known as Atria.

TUCANA
Chart 3, 4; RA 23h dec −60°; January
A southern constellation, found between Achernar, in Eridanus, and Peacock, in Pavo. Its brightest star is of third magnitude. Tucana contains the Small Magellanic Cloud, one of two small galaxies in orbit around our own Galaxy, which we see as the Milky Way.

URSA MAJOR
Charts 2, 5, 6; RA 12h dec 50°; February
Seven of the brightest stars of this large constellation together form the asterism known as the Plough or Big Dipper, the most familiar pattern of the northern sky. Circumpolar from London, only the 'handle' stars are visible, and then rather low in the north, on nights in April and May from southerly latitudes. The fainter stars which make up the Great Bear's legs, extending towards Leo, are somewhat higher.

URSA MINOR
Chart 6; RA 16h dec 80°
Ursa Minor contains the north celestial pole, marked by second-magnitude Polaris. Like all other stars, Polaris actually revolves around the pole, but it is so close to the pole that its motion is negligible. The other bright star in Ursa Minor, also of second magnitude, is Kochab. The constellation is always below the horizon from southerly latitudes.

VELA
Charts 1, 5; RA 9h dec −50°; January
A southern constellation, lying on the Milky Way to the north of Carina.

VIRGO
Charts 2, 5; RA 13h dec 0°
The second-largest of the constellations, Virgo lies on the celestial equator and is one of the 12 star groups of the zodiac. Its brightest star is blue first-magnitude Spica, which makes up an almost equilateral triangle with Arcturus and Denebola. From Spica, the constellation extends to the west towards Leo and to the east in the direction of Serpens and Libra. Virgo is best placed for observation in late autumn.

VOLANS
Chart 1; RA 8h dec −70°

VULPECULA
Chart 3; RA 20h dec 20°